INAUGURATED
PRESIDENT

WE SHALL PAY ANY PRICE,
BEAR ANY BURDEN, MEET
ANY HARDSHIP, SUPPORT
ANY FRIEND, OPPOSE
ANY FOE TO ASSURE THE
SURVIVAL OF LIBERTY

JOHN F. KENNEDY

JANUARY 20,
1961

THE WORLD'S TRIBUTE
TO JOHN F. KENNEDY
IN MEDALLIC ART

Medals, Coins and Tokens—
An Illustrated
Standard Reference

THE
WORLD'S TRIBUTE
TO
JOHN F.
KENNEDY
IN
MEDALLIC ART

by Aubrey Mayhew

William Morrow & Company, Inc.
New York 1966

For Laura J. Hall

CONTENTS

Medallic Art Defined   ix

Acknowledgments   xiii

Introduction   xv

Purpose and Definition   xix

Numbering System   xxi

JOHN F. KENNEDY   xxiii

PART I—UNITED STATES COINS, MEDALS,
TOKENS, AND RELATED ITEMS   3

PART II—FOREIGN MEDALS, COINS, AND
TOKENS, BY COUNTRY   91

     ARABIA   93

     AUSTRIA   99

     CANADA   105

     CHINA   111

     ENGLAND   115

     FRANCE   119

     GERMANY   123

     HOLLAND   152

     ITALY   156

     JAPAN   168

     MEXICO   172

     SOUTH AMERICA   181

     SWITZERLAND   185

     YUGOSLAVIA   189

Index   193

MEDALLIC ART DEFINED

The author feels the need to define the term medallic art for a number of reasons, the main one being that this book is somewhat different from most other books on numismatics and especially on medals. This is because of the universal interest in John F. Kennedy and the activity created in the various tributes to him. Perhaps more items of tribute have been issued for him in a shorter time than for any other person or subject. The interest stimulated by Kennedy necessitated this book and its early publication.

Normally, when one refers to medals or medallic art, we think of medallions or coinlike objects. This has been the rule, and rightly so. However, I do not feel that medallic art should be limited to such objects. In observing the elements that go into making a medal one notes that artists, engravers, sculptors, designers, and metal workers make up the art forms that medallic art relies on for its completion and beauty. Therefore, any work of art in metal from the hands of these artists should be considered medallic art.

I do not propose to change the face of medallic art, but rather to expand on it—with limitations, of course. I endorse the collection of medals as the basis for medallic art and/or medal collectors.

It will be noticed in the pages of this book that I have chosen certain items that normally would not be collectable as medallic art. The decision to include these items was not an easy one. The first question that entered my mind expressed the reaction of the serious collector: Should I expand an ageless hobby as set up and established by accomplished and knowledgable collectors? And, too, I risked the possibility of the book being construed as a catalog of general Kennedy items. I hope this will not be the case, because anyone familiar with John F. Kennedy and the thousands of plastic, paper, glass, and generally novel items issued and distributed since his death will surely know that this is not a book or catalog of Kennedy items as such. This is purely a book of medallic art.

Among the items referred to in this book which would not likely be found in the collection of a serious collector is the Kennedy Plaque, a copper portrait in a frame. This piece is a beautiful work of art, created by a person who works in metal. It is a numbered item and is issued in limited quantities. I cannot see how this can be classified as other than medallic art. Then we have the charms or key-ring medals. These were pressed, cast, molded, and etched. The workmanship is not the best, and they are not the most beautiful works of art. We cannot even say they are or were intended as tribute pieces with any significant meaning, that is, in our time. But they are metal, and there is a certain amount of artistic work involved: Who knows what meaning these pieces will have to future collectors.

In further defense of these items, consider the new collector who wishes to collect Kennedy but cannot afford the expensive, standard pieces of the series. This is an important consideration, especially for we who influence the Kennedy series.

Today, many young, new collectors are too quickly discouraged because of the expense involved in collecting a series, be it coins or medals. The commercialism of the hobby and those who deal in the items for a livelihood tend in many cases to disregard the beginner or the person with a limited budget. This results in the loss of potential collectors and, worse, persons who may develop into scholars and numismatists. I strongly endorse supporting the new collector and finding ways to induce him into our wonderful world of numismatics.

All of these matters were considered when I decided to expand on the field of medallic art. I excluded many items that are part of my personal collection for fear of being too extreme. However, I plan to include these items in a future edition or revision. The items I refer to are metal busts of Kennedy, additional plaques, and various other metal items.

I think, too, that items demonstrating the many ways a particular medal may be used for display purposes, such as paper weights, money clips, and desk plaques, eventually deserve a place in the series. These items are made for beauty and are practical. While this could be a never-ending subject, they do stop somewhere, and as time passes they become more scarce and therefore more appealing as collector items. The Kennedy series is and will continue to be an adventure of immeasurable pleasure. The expanse of the subject is unsurpassed by any other numismatic subject. Serious thought should go into the decision of collecting Kennedy items because of the many facets involved.

However you decide to approach the series, I think you should limit yourself to areas with a purpose and a plan. I assume that if you are reading this you have decided upon or are considering the medallic art of Kennedy. If this is true, do not shortchange yourself by not including all items of metal as a part of your collection. You may even find this a good way to begin. It is my strong belief that the items I refer to as not usually included as medallic art will be the hardest to acquire in the years to come. The medals made of precious metal will be preserved and collected, but the novel, general, or commercial product will be limited to sales value as decided by the nonmedalist manufacturer. When his consumer demand ceases, he will discontinue the sales and likely destroy his remaining stock and go on to the next product. This also implies that the novel items will not be as sought after or preserved because they were originally purchased by noncollectors. When the novelty wears off they will be discarded. This should indicate the eventual scarcity of these items.

I would like to point out a fact of experience: there are some two thousand jewelry manufacturers in the city of New York. The majority of these firms issued one type or another of Kennedy medal, key ring or charm. These pieces were distributed for sale in New York only. In fact, I learned that the consumer demand for these items was very limited and most merchants ordered small quantities and never reordered. Most people have never seen these items nor will they ever see them. I attempted to track down each of these manufacturers but had to stop because of the extent of the endeavor. I had wanted to include these items in this book. I hope eventually to see every one of them.

Among the many items one might consider or include in their collection of medallic art is metal spoons. We know that spoon collecting is a popular hobby in itself, but if a spoon is made that relates to the subject of a collection, and it is an artistic work in metal, then it should be included. (I am sure this will create a stir among the old-timers.)

To restate my position on this matter, I define any work of art that is executed in metal as medallic art which should be collected if related to a particular series. This will increase one's field, knowledge, and collection and will stimulate one's interest.

ACKNOWLEDGMENTS

A special acknowledgment to these men who may not even be aware of their contribution to this book. These people are a credit to numismatics:

Andrew T. Faller
Hans M. F. Schulman
William Fox Steinberg

To Dr. Gerald Jay Steinberg of Silver Spring, Maryland, whose kindness and friendship helped to make this book worthwhile. Dr. Steinberg loaned many of the items shown in this book for reference and made it possible to photograph them. Dr. Steinberg is a collector and student of Kennedy items. His interests include every area of the subject, and from my experience he is the most active collector and possesses the largest general collection of Kennedy items known to me.

And to the many people too numerous to list to whom I owe my thanks: collectors, manufacturers, medalists, trade papers and friends. And to:

Fred Baron, translations;
Mickey Crofford, photography;
Ward Crowley, collection;
Andrew T. Faller, photography.

A. M.

INTRODUCTION

This book is a tribute and memorial to our late President John Fitzgerald Kennedy; a great man who gave his life for his country and its people; a man loved and admired throughout the world by all people, who achieved much in his short time as the 35th President of the United States but did not have time to do the numerous things he was capable of doing.

This work contains a record of the medallic art struck because of John F. Kennedy for the benefit of numismatists, numismatics, and history. Written at a time when the items referred to were readily available and easy to acquire, it is a permanent record of how the world felt about this man. This art form is used by many to express their feelings.

Usually, books of this type are written years after the medals and tokens are issued, thus presenting a great deal of doubt as to identification, origin, and authenticity. Therefore, this type of work becomes invaluable to collectors of Kennedy medallic art and to historians.

I have included every available issue known to me up to the time of publication, including foreign and domestic issues. I will, of course, continue the cataloguing of new items issued for a second volume of this work.

From the time President Kennedy was assassinated, I began to collect the medals, coins, and tokens as they were issued solely for the purpose of writing this book. They were invaluable in the research, and possession of the actual items gave me a greater knowledge of the subject. Working with the individual medal allows a thorough working knowledge of the subject and enables a greater projection into the meaning and purpose of the tribute by those who issued the medals.

All of the issues listed here were not intended or struck as commemoratives but are presented as such for obvious reasons. Each medal as presented will be explained in detail as to purpose and intent.

Some are official, but others are the product of commercial merchandisers who sought to profit from a nation's shock at the tragic event that took the life of its President. This cannot be helped or corrected in this book; however, we can explain the reasons.

Many of the pieces have little or no meaning and some are

very significant. Of course, they will all become meaningful with time.

I feel that the striking of many of these items was not warranted and that President Kennedy parallels Abraham Lincoln in that both were martyred by minorities for reasons that served their own immediate purposes. Of course, these minorities were strong, either politically or financially and were, therefore, able to accomplish an almost impossible feat of immortalizing these Presidents. This was not necessary, however, since both deserved immortality and would have been placed in greatness on their own achievements and merit. This is proven by the striking of the United States half dollar of 1964 depicting President Kennedy. It is a truly deserving and appropriate tribute. President Lyndon B. Johnson is to be commended for his historical decision and act of using his influence and direction with the United States Congress in this matter.

I would venture to guess that the commemorative medals, coins, tokens, and miscellaneous metal items to be issued in future years will triple the number listed in this book. I plan a revision of this book when feasible and practical.

Regardless of the validity of the issues, they are and will become memorials to John F. Kennedy for reasons of time and history. And, too, we cannot overlook the value to collectors and numismatists of today and tomorrow. The memory of John F. Kennedy will grow, and every facet of his life will become even more important to future generations. In the years to come there will be a great number of these items available in uncirculated condition because of the popularity of the subject. Today, there are thousands of collectors for these items, but many of the people accumulating them are not true collectors and, after a time, they will sell or pass them on either because they will lose interest or will hope to profit by their sale.

The rarity estimate given in each instance is based on the number issued and demand for each at this time. However, values have not been placed on the pieces; this is done in the annual companion pamphlet because values will increase on the items.

This increase in the value of the items is not, although it may appear to be, contradictory to the previous statement

xvi

that the pieces will become available in uncirculated condition. But there will be difficulty in acquiring certain pieces because a number of the issues were commercial failures and were struck in very limited quantities. In some cases, where only the trial pieces were struck, it will be increasingly difficult to complete a collection. This, in turn, will increase the value of many pieces.

I have been conservative in each description and as accurate as possible as to the amounts struck or the rarity.

After studying this book, a new collector might be discouraged from starting a collection of Kennedy because of the quantity of individual pieces or the scarcity of many. If this is the case, I urge him to reconsider. Because of the many different categories and countries, the Kennedy series may be collected like coins; that is, the collection may be grouped by country or by official issues or by nonofficial issues. A type set can even be made because of the hundreds of varieties. In any case, I urge the interested to pursue a study of the series, for it is a wide education on President Kennedy and a most satisfying personal fulfillment.

To the advanced collector, I cannot imagine a more interesting series or a more challenging one. One of my most rewarding and personal experiences has been the collecting and studying of the medals and the writing of this book.

A. M.

PURPOSE AND DEFINITION

The purpose of this book is to give quantities struck and available and the origin of each piece. This type of work assists the collector in locating material and gives him a basis for his collection. It also establishes the facts surrounding each piece for future numismatists.

My approach here is to classify the items by their current importance and type of issue: United States medals, coins, tokens, and related items; foreign medals, coins, and tokens—by country.

All metals and sizes are described. Different type issues are combined, that is, tokens, coins, medals, and related items. The numbering system, which it is hoped will become the standard for the Kennedy items, is originated in a way that differs from most other systems but, I hope, will be more convenient and efficient. Each item is given a number, beginning with the most precious metal. For example, a gold of an issue is 100, the silver is 100-A, and the bronze is 100-B. If two medals appear the same in design but differ in size, the next size is given a different number. In the case of pieces that were struck with loops and also struck without loops, these are listed in the same sections. The reason for this is that some issues were intended as official or semiofficial issues but were later holed or looped for novel reasons or duplicated for commercial purposes. This system allows for additions of the same items without necessitating different numbers in subsequent revisions.

All plates are standard size and show obverse and reverse sides. The piece shown is the most precious metal of the issue available, but is not referred to.

This work is not a catalog of Presidential or political items, but rather those of medallic art or numismatic interest.

There is one point that I would like to clarify before it becomes an issue with the reader of this book. I have entitled the book *The World's Tribute to John F. Kennedy in Medallic Art,* and then I list medals or tokens that do not appear as tribute items. The explanation for this is simple. This book is not written only for the current market and those still experiencing the shock of President Kennedy's death but for the many future generations who will not have experienced what we have and will hold the name of John F. Kennedy as a great person in American history with no more personal attachment than they will have for any other historical figure. Therefore, it is my contention that each and every medal and token struck for President Kennedy will become a tribute because of its very nature, regardless of its original purpose. An example is the items struck as political pieces before his passing. These certainly were not tribute items, but they have become such because they are mementoes to be collected and cherished by all who loved President Kennedy. In any case, each of these items have a definite historical value and serve to compose the total.

NUMBERING SYSTEM

It is hoped that the titles and numbers given to the items listed in this book will be used by the collector, researcher, and historian. No demand or requirement is made for this; however, it is requested by the author that those persons making reference to these items will use the correct titles and numbers.

JOHN F. KENNEDY

This section, which is usually reserved for biographical review, will be changed slightly. I think enough information is available in print to give a detailed biography of John F. Kennedy for those who want additional reading matter on our late President.

Rather, I will take this opportunity to reflect and project, from the viewpoint of one who was close to the period when President Kennedy was alive, on how he relates to numismatics in the present time and how he will relate in the future.

John F. Kennedy was an unusual man for many reasons, some obvious and others not. He seemed to appear from nowhere on the national political scene. At least, this was my initial reaction. However, a close look reveals a man with a tremendously disciplined and coordinated life. Kennedy was a man meticulously prepared and equipped for any undertaking. His every thought and movement seemed planned before its execution—predetermined by a total dedication to whatever the end was to be. A quick review of the man, rather than the influence of his publicity and commercial coverage by the news media and various authors, reveals an amazing and quite remarkable person. There are many who will disagree, who think they knew the man or who would judge him by his brief tenure as President. But he really was only completing his apprenticeship when he was killed.

The old saying, "A man is the sum total of his past," is especially relevant to the life of John F. Kennedy. If one were to evaluate Kennedy's past and the period of his Presidency from a clinical standpoint and then project his future, he might emerge as the greatest man of our century. Few single events in the history of the world had the impact of stimulating a reaction from every major country and ethnic group as did the assassination and now the life of John F. Kennedy. This is obvious by the medallic art issued for him.

The period of his life most analyzed is the short span of his Presidency. From this, many will evaluate the man and his acts. If this is done, a great injustice will be done to John F. Kennedy, for he was a man who did not have enough time.

The acts he performed during this short period are not important; this is one case where the intention was foremost. I think the true Kennedy is yet to be known, and will be revealed in the present and future medallic art to be issued for him.

Medals have a way of telling a truer story than the printed word. In medallic art, we tend to be more precise because space does not allow anything but the most explicit points. A medal series is difficult to draw from until enough medals have been issued to present a picture. Perhaps this is the reason so many years pass before a series on a particular subject becomes established or recognized.

With the exception of Abraham Lincoln, none of the other United States Presidents who were assassinated (Lincoln, William McKinley and William Garfield), had the impact on the people that John F. Kennedy had. I think that based on the interest created in Kennedy, the importance of his passing will grow to exceed even that of Lincoln. Therefore, I predict an increase in medallic art of a greater significance than we know now. The Kennedy series should become the most popular that numismatics has known. The individual pieces should become the most sought after by collectors, numismatists, and historians. There is little doubt that the Kennedy series is destined to be the rich man's series. This is apparent by the very nature of the subject and the total number of items that are being turned out in Europe where there are not the gold restrictions we have in the United States. Many of the gold issues are low mintage (fifty struck in some cases), and the fact that they are gold already puts them in a higher price bracket. These items will be the first to increase in value, and the collector who wishes to complete his collection will wait for these items to appear in catalogs and at auctions, as these are the places where prices will be established. This does not restrict the collector who wants to collect Kennedy because he can collect type sets, such as the silver issues. But it *is* a rich man's series.

The Lincoln, Washington, and Columbus series are the ranking collections today. Certainly, these items were collected from their inception, but I doubt that they gained any popularity until many years later. As the medals, coins, and tokens were issued on each, we began to unfold history and the true character of the person; hence they became an attraction for numismatists, collectors, and historians. There are more catalogs and reference books on these subjects than on any other individuals or series today. A single indication of Kennedy's popularity and impact is the fact that at this time there are at least twenty-five thousand serious Kennedy series collectors and as many as one hundred thousand persons who have collected some items. It is estimated that there are twenty thousand people who will buy anything issued on Kennedy, including books and souvenirs.

In addition to this book, we can expect to see many more works by students of the series.

I plan to continue the cataloging of new items and to do extensive research into each medal and its background. A second volume will be published from my files, which have become increasingly comprehensive. New information will be acquired on the pieces included here and on all new issues.

PART I

UNITED STATES COINS, MEDALS, TOKENS, AND RELATED ITEMS

KENNEDY UNITED STATES
HALF DOLLAR 1964

A bill proposed by President Lyndon B. Johnson and passed by an act of the 86th Congress authorized the replacement of the Franklin Half Dollar with this coin. Since Kennedy's popularity and the tragic circumstances resulted in these coins becoming collector's items the first year of issue, they were sought after by nearly every person who had heard of John F. Kennedy. In fact, the coin never went into circulation because of the public demand for mementoes.

The mintage of the Kennedy Half Dollar for a two-year period—1964-65, but dated 1964 only—is 387,835,450, the largest ever struck for a United States half dollar. All of these coins are silver. On December 30, 1965, the Denver Mint began striking this half dollar in the newly authorized "Clad Coin" with the date of "1965." However, these were held until 1966.

In 1964, the coin was struck as a regular issue in single pieces and also as part of the 1964 proof and mint sets. Proof sets amounting to 3,375,065 were struck and 977,410 mint sets were issued in 1964. Mint and proof sets were not made in 1965.

The obverse depicts a bust of Kennedy, facing left. Above is inscribed "LIBERTY" and below are the words "IN GOD WE TRUST/1964."

The reverse of this coin bears the United States seal, above which is inscribed "UNITED STATES OF AMERICA" and below, "HALF DOLLAR." The edge is reeded.

The coin was designed and engraved by Gilroy Roberts, Chief Engraver of the United States Mint at Philadelphia, Pennsylvania.

Two oddities of the Kennedy Half Dollar have been found to date. One, found in a roll of halves, has the exact weight of a 1964 quarter but is not a perfect circle, having rather an oblong shape. It is larger in diameter and thinner than a quarter. The second oddity is a laminated piece in which a thin layer of metal peeled. The peeled area is much shinier than the balance of the piece. This is common in cents and nickels but rare in halves and silver dollars.

3

NO.	QUANTITY	SIZE	DESCRIPTION	ORIGINAL PRICE
1	Unlimited	.50	Silver	$ .50
1-A	Unlimited	.50	Clad coin	.50
1-B	3,375,065		Proof set, 1964—sealed pack, 5 pieces	2.10
1-C	977,410		Mint set, 1964—sealed pack, 10 pieces	
1-D	Unlimited	.50	Silver, goldplated	1.00
1-E		.50	Silver, proof single	

KENNEDY UNITED STATES PROOF SET 1964

JOHN F. KENNEDY
INAUGURAL MEDAL 1961

This medal, the official Presidential medal of John F. Kennedy, was the work of Gilroy Roberts, Chief Engraver of the United States Mint, and his assistant, Frank Gasparro.

Struck at the Philadelphia Mint, the 3-inch bronze medal, with the President's name and profile on the obverse, is one of the traditional Presidential series of Mint medals.

The reverse bears the Presidential seal and, from his inaugural speech, the following words: "WE SHALL PAY ANY PRICE, BEAR ANY BURDEN, MEET ANY HARDSHIP, SUPPORT ANY FRIEND, OPPOSE ANY FOE TO ASSURE THE SURVIVAL OF LIBERTY."

The obverse of the Presidential medal was used for the 1962 Assay Commission medals.

The Presidential medal pictured here is available from Superintendent, Philadelphia Mint, Philadelphia, Pennsylvania.

NO.	QUANTITY	SIZE	DESCRIPTION	ORIGINAL PRICE
2	Unlimited	76mm	Bronze	$3.00

THE KENNEDY-JOHNSON MEDAL

An issue of inaugural size, Executive Branch, Kennedy-Johnson medals were issued January 29, 1962, by Executive Designs, Inc., P.O. Box 226, Pemberton, New Jersey.

The double portrait of John F. Kennedy and Lyndon B. Johnson is in bas-relief; the Inaugural Committee gave permission to the firm to coordinate the obverse with a reverse design by Philip Kraczkowski. This noted sculptor was commissioned to do the Kennedy-Johnson medal, the first issue of the Executive Branch series.

The Robbins Company of Attleboro, Massachusetts, was appointed manufacturer by the Board of Directors of Executive Designs, Inc., thus combining seventy years of experience in high relief production with outstanding design and the finest quality.

The obverse was originally used for an Inaugural Committee medal. One unit manufactured was in 14k gold and was presented to the then Vice-President, Lyndon Johnson. Permission was obtained from the commission to use the obverse with a reverse designed by Philip Kraczkowski who had been commissioned to do the double portrait of Kennedy and Johnson that appears on the obverse.

The reverse bears the seal of the Office of the Vice-President (right) and of the President (left). Above is the legend: "JOHN FITZGERALD KENNEDY/35th PRESIDENT 1961," and below is the design: "37th VICE PRESIDENT/ LYNDON BAINES JOHNSON."

An error appeared in this medal and has caused a great deal of confusion as to how it happened and exactly what the error was.

The following information gives an accurate account of the matter. There were some of the bronze and silver issues struck with Lyndon Johnson listed as the 38th Vice-President of the United States when he was the 37th Vice-President.

The total number of error pieces that were released for sale were 70 silver medals and 150 bronze medals. These medals were shipped to dealers Tom Wass of New York City and Joe Welles of Topeka, Kansas.

The error was a die mistake which was caught by the Robbins Company on the twelfth day of manufacture and on the first day the numbering of the medals was started.

One employee began numbering the medals by hand, a second employee began numbering another group of medals when the error was discovered and this explains the skip in numbers of the error. The balance of the error-struck medals was scrapped and melted down. The few that were misnumbered slipped through and were shipped.

Authorization for the striking of the medal came from the White House and from the Vice-President's office in addition to the Inaugural Committee's authorization.

One 14k gold medal was struck and presented to Lyndon B. Johnson.

The total mintage includes those medals which were struck with the error.

NO.	QUANTITY	SIZE	DESCRIPTION	ORIGINAL PRICE
3	Unique	70mm	Gold	Presentation piece
3-A	40	70mm	Silver, fine, .999, Nos. 1–40 error	$35.00
3-B	20	70mm	Silver, fine, .999, Nos. 51–70 error	35.00
3-C	10	70mm	Silver, fine, .999, Nos. 100–110 error	35.00
3-D	10	70mm	Silver, fine, .999, Nos. 41–50 correct	35.00
3-E	30	70mm	Silver, fine, .999, Nos. 71–100 correct	35.00
3-F	1,890	70mm	Silver, fine, .999, Nos. 111–2,000 correct	35.00
3-G	150	70mm	Bronze, 1–150 error	5.00
3-H	3,850	70mm	Bronze, 151–4,000 correct	5.00

ERROR

1962 ANNUAL ASSAY COMMISSION MEDAL

Struck and issued by the United States Mint at Philadelphia. Given to the members of the 1962 Assay Commission. (For details of Assay Commission, see no. 5.) The obverse is the same as no. 2. The edge is plain.

NO.	QUANTITY	SIZE	DESCRIPTION	ORIGINAL PRICE
4	27	37mm	Bronze	

1964 ANNUAL ASSAY COMMISSION MEDAL

The 1964 Annual Assay Commission Medal portrays President Lyndon B. Johnson on the obverse. The reverse of the bronze medal depicts the designing of the new Kennedy Half Dollar, which is reproduced in miniature.

The 1964 meeting of the Annual Assay Commission was held at the Philadelphia Mint on February 12, 1964. This annual assay, "The Trial of the Pyx," is a mandatory yearly examination of the past year's coinage of United States mints and is undertaken by persons not concerned with the Mint and was prescribed by legislation enacted in 1792.

Records show that it was adopted upon a recommendation by Alexander Hamilton, who prescribed the basic legislation upon which our monetary system is based. "The Trial of the Pyx" was first held in Britain, although authorities greatly disagree on when it was first instituted there.

The membership of the Annual Assay Commission is comprised by appointments made by the President. The number of these appointments numbered twenty-four in 1964, nearly half of those selected being prominent numismatists.

These members included Keeton Arnett, Cab Atkins, George Barlow, George H. Becht, Harry X. Boosel, Ernest F. Cooke, Mrs. Janet Sharon Farr, Mrs. Lucy W. Freeman, Mrs. Dorothy Gersheson, Joe E. Gonzales, Michael Granis, and Aubrey A. Gunnels.

Others serving included Reverend Noel F. Moholy, R. Bruce Morrison, Harry O. Nichols, Miss Virginia D. Peters, Paul E. Pontius, Russell B. Robins, Mrs. Margo Russell, Mark W. Saurs, John H. Sengstacke, Carl G. Taylor, Jack O. Yeager, and Richard S. Yeoman.

Acting as ex-officio members were the Honorable Thomas J. Clary, Judge of the District Court for the Eastern District of Pennsylvania, the Honorable James J. Saxon, Comptroller of the Currency, and Mr. Paul J. Maguire, Assayer of the United States Assay Office in New York City. Mr. Pontius, who is with the Bureau of Standards, carried with him to Philadelphia a set of weights which had been calibrated against the standard weights of the bureau. These weights, calibrated for the coins which were being assayed, were used in the testing of the coins.

The ceremony is believed to have been originated by the Greeks and taken up by the Romans as they checked on their mint masters. The United States followed Britain in the practice.

The medal was struck at the United States Mint in Philadelphia and was distributed to the Assay Commission members. The obverse consists of the same design as that used in the Presidential Series Medal offered by the United States Mint. A large bust of the President, facing left, is shown. Around the medal is the legend, "LYNDON B. JOHNSON," and raised on the truncation of the bust is the designer's name and the date, "GILROY ROBERTS, 1963." The reverse, designed by Edward Grove, shows a hand holding the new Kennedy Half Dollar with assaying equipment depicted in the background. Above is the legend, "UNITED STATES MINT AT PHILADELPHIA"; below is inscribed, "ANNUAL ASSAY/COMMISSION/1964." The edge is plain.

NO.	QUANTITY	SIZE	DESCRIPTION
5	33	57mm	Bronze

JOHN FITZGERALD KENNEDY MEMORIAL MEDAL

In 1963, President Kennedy personally approved the Presidential Art Design for the medal illustrated above to be used as a campaign medal during the Presidential election campaign of 1964—a singular recognition of numismatics by an American President. Unfortunately, the use of this campaign medal never transpired because of President Kennedy's untimely death.

In President Kennedy's memory, Presidential Art Medals, Inc., Englewood, Ohio, issued the Kennedy Campaign Medal in modified form to show 1963, the terminal date of office, as a Kennedy Memorial Medal.

This medal was sculptured in very high relief by the noted sculptor Ralph J. Menconi.

The obverse depicts the bust of Kennedy facing three quarters right. Above and around the outer rim is written: "JOHN FITZGERALD KENNEDY." To the left of the bust is an Eternal Flame, and to the right are the dates "1917—1963."

The reverse portrays the three phases of his public life: First, the PT Boat 109 and his naval officer's insignia; second, the Massachusetts state seal representing his Senatorial service and; third, the Presidential seal commemorating his tenure of Presidency. These portions are separated by oak leaves (signifying strength) and laurel leaves (signifying eternity).

The medal was struck in both silver and bronze; however, the bronze was struck only in 1964.

NO.	QUANTITY	SIZE	DESCRIPTION	ORIGINAL PRICE
6	15,000	38mm	Silver, .999	$15.00
6-A	20,000 (approximately)	38mm	Bronze	5.00

FOUR ASSASSINATED PRESIDENTS

Presidential Art Medals of Englewood, Ohio, is one of the leading medalists in America today. It has and is producing some of the finest medals and subjects we know. Presidential Art Medals have issued the now famous Presidential Series, the Statehood Series, the Signers of the Declaration of Independence Series, the John Fitzgerald Kennedy Medal, the Robert Frost Medal, the Sir Winston Churchill Memorial Medal, and the President Lyndon B. Johnson Official Inaugural Medal.

The artistic techniques used in every step of the manufacture of these beautiful medals is evident.

Now, in addition to the many medals mentioned already, Presidential Art Medals has issued a most beautiful, meaningful work of art. The above-depicted medal was issued in January, 1966. This medal is considered one of the finest artistic works ever offered by a medal company. Its design is rich and simple and a tribute to the man honored.

The obverse portrays an exceptional likeness of Lincoln, Kennedy, Garfield, and McKinley. Their signatures are incised below the portraits.

The reverse depicts the United States flag and the Presidential flag with the following inscription set in relief: "PRESIDENTS OF THE UNITED STATES OF AMERICA WHO GAVE THEIR LIVES IN DEVOTIONAL SERVICE TO THIS NATION." Dates of each President and the Presidential seal are in raised relief.

The sculptor is the distinguished sculptor and designer Ralph J. Menconi.

The medal was announced and sold by mail through Presidential Art Medals; however, dealers did sell the medal. A descriptive pamphlet and metal desk holder were included with each medal.

NO.	QUANTITY	SIZE	DESCRIPTION	ORIGINAL PRICE
7	1,000 numbered	70mm	Silver, .999+	$39.50
7-A	Unlimited, un-numbered	70mm	Antique bronze	5.00

PRESIDENTIAL ART MEDAL

This medal is the first in a series of Presidential Art Medals to be issued by the Presidential Art Medal Company, P.O. Box 187, Englewood, Ohio.

The sculptor of the Presidential Art Medal is Ralph J. Menconi. Menconi was commissioned for this work on the basis of his recognized skill in full portrait and high relief work.

Ralph Menconi was born in Union City, New Jersey, on June 15, 1915. He attended Acarborough Prep School at Hamilton College and was graduated from Yale University with the degree of Bachelor of Fine Arts in 1939. He was also graduated from the National Academy of Design, The L. C. Tiffany Foundation, Officers Candidate School, The Industrial College of the Armed Forces, and the Command and General Staff College.

He distinguished himself during World War II, serving a total of five years, three years of which were spent in the European theater of operations. He received seven battle participation awards, the units he commanded were twice cited for outstanding performance of duty, and he was awarded the Bronze Star. Menconi entered the Army as a private and was discharged as a major in the Corps of Engineers.

Menconi's work has earned for him many outstanding awards and commissions, including the Ellen P. Speyer Prize at the National Academy Annual Exhibition in 1941; The International Competition for the Imperial Palace, Addis Ababa, Ethiopia; The War Memorial, St. George School, Newport, Rhode Island; and The Jefferson National Expansion Memorial Competition, St. Louis, Missouri (in collaboration with Caleb Hornbostel and Associates). His medals, medallions, portraits, and tablets include The Iron and Steel Institute, The American Standards Association, The National Book Award, and Kenyon College and Eight Bells, Martha's Vineyard, Massachusetts. In addition, he was the designer of the official Alaskan Statehood Medal.

He is a member of the National Sculpture Society, The Municipal Art Society, The Architectural League of New York City, and Delta Upsilon Fraternity.

The Medallic Art Company of New York City prepared the dies and struck the pieces.

Presidential Art Company is one of the few manufacturers of medals which have adhered to a strict policy of quality in subject and design. To date, they have issued additional pieces in the Presidential series and have added the Signers of the Declaration of Independence Series, the Statehood Series, the John Fitzgerald Kennedy Memorial Medal, No. 7, the Lyndon B. Johnson Inaugural Medal, and the Winston Churchill Memorial Medal—plus various chains and pendants.

These medals were issued by Presidential Art in various novel forms, such as lucite timer, paper weights, lucite key rings, and a desk top paper holder.

The listing of unique items was done only because they are out of the manufacturer's possession and could become available to a collector, although this is not likely.

The goldplated listing is included because these pieces are available. They are not official issues of the manufacturer. Rather, they are processed by commercial enterprisers.

The unfinished piece in bronze and listed as unique is information furnished by the author based on his knowledge of the item. When Medallic Art Company strikes a medal, the medal is processed with a "finish" on the surface of the medal. Unless a medal receives this finish, either in bronze or silver, it is not released to the public. However, one known piece did leave the Medallic Art Company "unfinished" and has been seen. No others are known to exist.

Platinum, gold and silver pieces are serially numbered.

Also issued at the 1964 American Numismatic Convention, Cleveland, Ohio, by the Presidential Art Medals Company was a series of Presidential Art chains, 26mm in diameter.

NO.	QUANTITY	SIZE	DESCRIPTION	ORIGINAL PRICE
8	10	32mm	Platinum	$500.00
8-A	150	32mm	Gold	
8-B	6,500	32mm	Silver, .999	10.00
8-C	Unlimited	32mm	Bronze	2.50
8-D	Unique	32mm	Bronze (variety), unfinished metal	

8-E	Unique		Sculptor's model
8-F		10 inches	Galvano, reproduction of original model presented to JFK by Presidential Art Medals Company
8-G		26½ × 15½ inches 10-inch medal	Presidential art Galvano, bronze	200.00
8-H		13 × 15 inches 10-inch medal	Galvano, bronze	100.00
8-I		8 step	Process set	35.00

KENNEDY-POPE JOHN PEACE MEDAL

This medal commemorates two outstanding Roman Catholics and world leaders, Pope John XXIII and the late President John F. Kennedy.

Both of these men who died in 1963 will be remembered in history for their part in the cause of world peace, which is the theme of this medal.

Pope John XXIII was the 261st Pope of the Roman Catholic Church. One of his last and most important acts was to bring the separated Christian churches together, for the first time in four hundred years, at the Second Vatican Council.

President Kennedy originated and put in force the Peace Corps.

The obverse shows profiles of Pope John XXIII and John F. Kennedy. Around the busts is the legend: "1958–1963 JOHN XXIII/JOHN F. KENNEDY 1961–1963." These dates indicate their terms in office.

The reverse depicts St. Peter's Basilica in Rome and the White House in Washington, D.C., in relief with rays emanating from behind. The legend is "CHRISTIAN UNITY/CIVIL LIBERTY/PEACE."

The medal was designed and issued by Frank Amato, Sr., of Portland, Oregon.

The sculptor is the artist and medalist Albino Manca of New York City.

Medallic Art Company, 325 East 45th Street, New York City, prepared the dies and struck the piece.

Sales were made through the mail from Mount Angel Abbey, St. Benedict, Oregon.

The mintage of this medal is questionable. The original information was that 1,500 bronze pieces would be struck and only 50 silver pieces. Soon after that announcement, it was learned that the silver issue was increased to 100 struck but not guaranteed. It was also stated that if the 1,500 bronze pieces did not satisfy the demand, more would be struck. Therefore, the original information released to the public was incorrect and misleading. This is a beautiful and meaningful medal and it is unfortunate that the persons in control of the striking were not guided by the general practice of the hobby to limit the striking and to give accurate information.

NO.	QUANTITY	SIZE	DESCRIPTION	ORIGINAL PRICE
9	100	63mm	Silver, .999	$35.00
9-A	1,500	63mm	Bronze	5.00

THE JOHN F. KENNEDY
MEMORIAL CITIZENSHIP
AWARD MEDAL

Sachs Quality Stores, Inc., with executive offices located at 330 Bruckner Boulevard, Bronx, New York, and eight branch stores in the metropolitan New York area, commenced a Citizenship Award Program in 1964.

The award is in the form of a bronze medal presented semi-annually to graduates of public, parochial, and vocational high schools in the metropolitan New York area.

The students are recommended to Sachs Committee by his or her school faculty. The medal honors the student for outstanding work in the field of citizenship. Many of the recipients are active in their school governments, organizing school and community activities. Others do volunteer work for city hospitals; several offer their services to charities or are active leaders in scouting organizations.

The medal was presented for the first time in June of 1964 to fifty-three students. The award was again given in January of 1965 to fourteen midyear graduates and, in June of 1965, 288 students were honored.

This is a beautiful, well-executed medal and a true tribute to John F. Kennedy.

Sachs Quality Stores are furniture outlets and are to be highly commended for their part in this type of activity.

The medal was designed and manufactured by the staff of Osborne-Kemper-Thomas, Inc., 110 E. 42nd St., New York City, for Sachs, and there were no trial pieces made.

The obverse depicts John F. Kennedy; the reverse is plain.

Sachs Quality Stores intends to continue presenting this medal on a semiannual basis. Therefore, the quantity given here is as of the date of publication.

NO.	QUANTITY	SIZE	DESCRIPTION
10	295	76mm	Bronze

MANSHIP MEDAL

THE OFFICIAL INAUGURAL MEDAL COMMEMORATING THE INAUGURATION OF JOHN FITZGERALD KENNEDY AS 35TH PRESIDENT OF THE UNITED STATES OF AMERICA JANUARY 20, 1961

An official inaugural medal is struck every four years to commemorate the inauguration of the President of the United States. The medal is an official inaugural souvenir.

One medal is struck in gold and presented to the President. This year, 1961, silver replicas were struck and serially numbered. Numbers 1 through 10 were reserved for members of the new President's Cabinet. Bronze medals were struck unnumbered.

Paul Manship, the artist who designed the 1961 medal, met twice with President John F. Kennedy to work on the portrait, and Mrs. John F. Kennedy was consulted by the Medal Design Committee on both the design and patina of the 1961 medal.

The first official inaugural medal was struck in 1901 for the second inauguration of President McKinley. The custom of striking a medal to commemorate the inauguration of a President is the outgrowth of badges that were presented to the President.

Since the inauguration of President Hoover, the replicas in bronze and silver have been made available to the public by popular demand. The value of these replicas has increased to such an extent that some of the early bronze medals are worth many times their original cost.

The design of the 1961 inaugural medal is traditional in that its face bears only a profile portrait of President John F. Kennedy and his name.

On the reverse is the Presidential seal, which is making its first appearance on an inaugural medal. Previously, the seal of the United States has been used on medals.

Only in 1909 and 1957 did the inaugural medals bear portraits of both the President and Vice-President.

The Presidential seal, which appears on the reverse of the 1961 inaugural medal, was originated during the administration of President Hayes. Apparently, it was an erroneous rendering of the Great Seal of the United States. Until 1945, during the administration of President Truman, the eagle in the Presidential seal faced its own left in contrast to heraldic custom. President Truman ordered that in the future the eagle face its own right and that the olive branches held in its right talon be a symbol of peace. The stars circling the eagle represent the states and now number fifty. No single star represents any particular state.

The 1961 inaugural medal is the second such medal to be designed by sculptor Paul Manship. His first inaugural medal was for Franklin D. Roosevelt in 1933 and bore the ship of state on the reverse.

Manship has often been referred to as the Dean of American Sculptors and is a noted lecturer and teacher. He was born in St. Paul, Minnesota, on Christmas Eve in 1885. He studied art in his native city as a boy and later at the Pennsylvania Academy of Fine Arts. At the age of twenty-three, he won the prize scholarship of the American Academy in Rome, where he worked for three years. He has executed many monuments, garden sculptures, portrait busts, relief sculptures, and medals. He has contributed to the *Encyclopaedia Britannica* on "The History of Sculpture" and has been awarded many medals of honor, among them that of the National Institute of Arts and Letters and the Medal of Honor of the National Sculpture Society. He is a Chevalier of the French Legion of Honor and a corresponding member of the Institute of France; he is also a member of the National Academy of Fine Arts of Argentina and of the National Academy of San Luca of Italy. He is Honorary President of the National Sculpture Society and a past president of the American Academy of Arts and Letters and of The Century Association of New York. He is chairman of the Smithsonian Commission of Fine Arts.

MANSHIP MEDAL

His principal works are to be seen in Cochran Memorial Park, St. Paul; Fort Wayne, Indiana; The Metropolitan Museum of Art, New York; The American Academy in Rome; American Cemetery, Thiaucort, France; The American Military Cemetery, Anzio, Italy; Brookgreen Gardens; Salmagundi Club, New York; Zoological Park, New York; Philips Academy, Andover, Massachusetts; Rockefeller Center, New York; League of Nations, Geneva, Switzerland; Norton Gallery of Art; University of Florida, Gainesville; and the Coliseum, New York.

Bids were taken for the production of the 1961 inaugural medal and the contract for manufacture of the medal was awarded to the Medallic Art Company of New York. The company has been described as the foremost firm of medalists in the United States. Distribution is being handled by Coin and Currency, Inc., of New York, except in the Washington, D.C., area where the Inaugural Medal Committee has reserved rights for distribution.

NO.	QUANTITY	SIZE	DESCRIPTION
11	Unique	70mm	Gold
11-A	7,500	70mm	Silver, .999
	Unlimited		
11-B	Approximately 20,000		Bronze

MANSHIP MEDAL
PROCESS SET

In addition to the regular issue of the Manship Inaugural Medal, Coin and Currency, Inc., ordered Medallic Art to strike the various steps of the striking process from the blank to the finished medal, with a total of six pieces to the set. The steps were the blank plachet, first blow, second blow, third blow, trimmed medal, and finished medal. The process was done only in bronze. A total of forty sets were made for distribution to the sales outlets of Coin and Currency for display and promotional purposes. The sets were eventually sold to individuals, although they were not originally intended for sale. As part of the process set the obverse and reverse copies of the sculptor's original model is also included in plaster.

NO.	QUANTITY	SIZE	DESCRIPTION
11-C	40	70mm	Process set (with molds)
11-D			Bronze, process set
11-E			Plaster molds
11-F	40		Blank planchet
11-G	40		First strike
11-H	40		Second strike
11-I	40		Third strike
11-J	40		Trimmed metal
11-K	Unlimited		Finished bronze

Finished Bronze

Trimmed Metal

Third Strike

Second Strike

First Strike

Blank Planchet

Plaster Molds
(Replica)

NCS MEMORIAL COIN-MEDAL

The National Commemorative Society, 1617 John F. Kennedy Boulevard, Philadephia, Pennsylvania, issued this Kennedy Memorial Coin-Medal which was designed and completed by Anthony deFrancisci and was finished just three days before the death of the noted sculptor. Mr. deFrancisci passed away in his sleep on October 20, 1964, the victim of a heart attack. His fame dates back to 1921 for his design of the United States "Peace Dollar," and he was a leading sculptor until his death at seventy-seven years of age. This is deFrancisci's last work. He also designed the World War II Veterans Discharge Lapel Emblem which was given to more than sixteen million American ex-servicemen.

Other famous works of this noted artist were a gold medal presented by Congress to General John J. Pershing and a medal given by the American Institute of Mining and Metallurgical Engineers to former President Herbert Hoover.

Mr. deFrancisci was born in Palermo, Sicily. He began to develop his talents in childhood, carving with his father who was in the marble business. In 1903, he came to the United States.

The medal was privately struck by the National Commemorative Society (NCS), the foremost private organization which strikes medals. This is a membership organization with a total membership permanently limited to the original number of charter members, 5,252. Each NCS membership is individually owned. These are transferable but rarely offered for sale in an ever-increasing price market.

Each month NCS members select by ballot a subject of national historical significance to be commemorated four months later. A noted sculptor is commissioned to execute a commemorative coin-medal on the subject. The great medallic artists are used—Roberts, Vincze, deFrancisci, Weinman, Manca, Grove, Schlag, and so forth. When the dies are completed, one proof is struck for each NCS member. The proofs are English Crown size and weigh at least 400 grains. They are struck with a true proof surface at the Franklin Mint, a division of General Numismatics Corporation, under exacting conditions. The finest sterling silver is used, except for the first three proofs of each issue which are struck in solid platinum.

The first nine memberships (Nos. 0001 through 0009) and the last membership (No. 5,252) are honorary, not paid. Following is the list of recipients of the honorary membership medals:

No. 0001—platinum

Auctioned off each month for the benefit of an appropriate nonprofit organization.

No. 0002—platinum

Retained by the society for special exhibition.

No. 0003—platinum

Donated to the Smithsonian Institution Collection.

No. 0004—sterling silver

Donated to the American Numismatic Society Collection.

No. 0005—sterling silver

Donated to the American Numismatic Association Collection.

No. 0006—sterling silver

Donated to the Money Museum of the Chase Manhattan Bank.

No. 0007—sterling silver

Donated to the Money Museum of the National Bank of Detroit.

No. 0008—sterling silver

Donated to the Numismatic News Collection.

No. 0009—sterling silver

Donated each month to a special museum or organization particularly interested in the subject being commemorated.

No. 5,252—sterling silver

Mr. Joseph M. Segel, chairman of the NCS board, bought the last-numbered membership before the membership rolls closed (he and his wife also bought membership Nos. 0010 and 0011). Mr. Segel has since donated membership No. 5,252 back to the society. For the proof struck with this last number, each number is presented to the sculptor of the coin-medal.

A very close control is kept to be certain every piece struck is accounted for.

After each member receives his medal, the dies are destroyed and a notarized statement is filed to that effect. There are no extra pieces available to the public.

Each medal is accompanied by a "newsletter." This is important to the medal; it contains a picture and biography of the issue's sculptor and a brief story on the subject of the medal.

Membership rolls were closed on July 1, 1964. The only way to acquire a membership is to buy one from a member.

The medals are numbered on the reeded edge.

NO.	QUANTITY	SIZE	DESCRIPTION	ORIGINAL PRICE
12	3	38mm	Platinum	
12-A	5,252	38mm	Sterling silver	$6.60

KENNEDY MEMORIAL MEDAL
BY HERALDIC ART

The principal Heraldic Art series includes three issues a year. The medals are of United States half-dollar size but are substantially thicker. They commemorate important events and anniversaries in American history. The purpose is to carry on the tradition of the United States commemorative half dollar, with fine art and significant purpose.

The medals are subscribed to in advance by collectors, museums, and dealers. These persons receive a wholesale price in order to induce them to support the project.

The Kennedy Medal is the third of a series of "Occasional Pieces" produced at the request of subscribers to mark current topics in addition to the regular historical events. The medal is accompanied by an illustrated pamphlet.

The obverse of the medal, taken from an original sculpture, was designed by Walter A. Sinz, N.S.S.; the reverse was designed by R. T. McNamara. It was struck only in solid sterling silver by the Heraldic Art Company, P.O. Box 735, Cleveland, Ohio.

This medal is a part of Heraldic Art's "Current Event Series" and was issued in 1964.

Depicted on the obverse is a full-faced representation of the late President's bust. To the left of the bust are the dates "1917/1963," and arched above is the inscription "JOHN FITZGERALD KENNEDY."

The reverse depicts the Capitol building with the funeral cortege in the plaza in the foreground. Ranks of honor guards are seen on the steps with members of Congress assembled beneath the portico. Above is the legend "HOMAGE OF THE NATION" and below burns the eternal flame.

NO.	QUANTITY	SIZE	DESCRIPTION	ORIGINAL PRICE
13	5,300	33mm	Sterling silver	$3.95

KENNEDY CREDO MEDAL

Rod Taylor, owner and general manager of the R. J. Taylor's Production Tool Company, 1502 Washington Street, Davenport, Iowa, produced the Kennedy Credo Memorial Medal.

The Production Tool Company was organized in 1952 for the purpose of designing special production tools and gauges for the instrument industry. In 1954 a tool and gauge shop was put into operation to manufacture these special tools. The company then became engaged in experimental or prototype work, including work on the Nike missile, Mercury capsule, Gemini project, Apollo project, and the Mariner "C" space vehicle.

Following the inauguration of President Kennedy, Taylor designed a token using the famous "ASK NOT WHAT YOUR COUNTRY CAN DO FOR YOU. ASK WHAT YOU CAN DO FOR YOUR COUNTRY."

On the obverse of the token were the words: "BUY AMERICAN PRODUCTS," with the name of the tool company that made the piece a modern store card.

The token was used as an advertising item and distributed throughout the country by Taylor. After a time, these pieces found their way around the world, even to the attention of the President himself.

After President Kennedy's death, Taylor began to receive requests for additional tokens. The decision was made to remove the advertising and replace it with a bust of Kennedy. The company had difficulty in locating a medal company that could strike the new medal and give an early delivery date. Consequently, Taylor then decided to strike the medal at his own company. He commissioned Gary Yarrington to sculpt the bust, and he began to install the necessary tooling for the striking.

It is interesting to note that this medal was done by inexperienced persons in the field of medallic manufacture and was the first medal to be made in the state of Iowa.

It seems that many persons and companies had a hand in the making and completion of the medal. Frizelle and Parsons Die Sinking Company of Moline, Iowa, made the dies. Deco Tool Supply and Globe Machinery and Supply Company also participated. Heat treating of the dies was done by Tri-City Heat Treat. Metal was acquired from the Central Steel and Wire Company. The aluminum came from Alcoa's mill in Riverdale, Iowa. The bronze blanks were dipped by Rock Island Plating. It seems that the actual striking was done on a one hundred ton press by the Uchtorff Company of Davenport. Further processes, such as aluminum anodizing, were done by Lunex of Pleasant Valley, Iowa; printing of the folders was done by Wagners Printing Company; and plastic holders were done by O and D Coin Shop and Linburg's.

Normally, the many steps in making a medal of this type are done by professionals and with less effort. We listed the people involved only because it is part of the history of a medal produced by people with a desire to create.

The first proof, struck in aluminum, was made December 24, 1963, and the bronze followed. Friends and customers received the first medals before January 1, 1964.

The medals, sculptured by Mr. Yarrington, the curator of exhibits at Davenport's public museum, were originally given as fund-raising items to the University of Nebraska Young Democrats; Loren Weatherax, chairman of the Great Plains Conference, 519 North 16th Street, Lincoln 8, Nebraska; and to Ken Lester, chairman of the College Young Democratic Clubs of America, Democratic National Committee, 1730 K Street, N.W., Washington, D.C. The only other outlet for the medals was Lauren Benson, 512-G Putnam Building, Davenport, Iowa, 52801.

NO.	QUANTITY	SIZE	DESCRIPTION	ORIGINAL PRICE
14		35mm	Silver, proof	$7.50
14-A		35mm	Silver, antique	7.50
14-B		35mm	Bronze, smooth	4.00
14-C		35mm	Bronze, antique	4.00
14-D		35mm	Aluminum	1.00
14-E		35mm	Trade token	.35

THE N.O.T.S. MEDAL

The N.O.T.S. Medal was struck to commemorate President Kennedy's visit to the United States Naval Ordnance Test Station at China Lake, California, on June 7, 1963. The medal was designed entirely by the civil service personnel employed at the installation.

Pieces were distributed initially to all civilian and military personnel employed at N.O.T.S. shortly after Kennedy's visit, which commemorated the twentieth anniversary of this naval station deep in the heart of the Mojave Desert.

The obverse is a profile bust of John F. Kennedy and was engraved from a three-dimensional plaster model sculptured by Charles B. Nardone, head of the graphic arts branch, Technical Information Department. The model was created from an original drawing developed from many photographs.

The reverse was designed by Lynn Nowels, head of the presentation art and design section of the graphic arts branch. The American eagle spreads its wings to protect the dove of peace, symbolizing the role played by the N.O.T.S., the Bureau of Naval Weapons, and the entire Navy. On the left side is a symbol of advanced computing machines used by the station's mathematicians, scientists, and engineers. Below to the right is a sunburst depicting the work done by Dr. Michelson in the field of the measurement of light.

The various elements used in the design of this medal were put together into an overall design through the collaboration of two other members of the staff of the publishing division of TID, W. S. Spafford, head of the editorial branch, and Richard Johnsen, an artist in the graphic arts branch. The exact words and elements used on each side of the medal were determined by Spafford, and their arrangement into the final product was the work of Johnsen.

NO.	QUANTITY	SIZE	DESCRIPTION	ORIGINAL PRICE
5	6,500		Goldine	$7.50

THE KENNEDY-JOHNSON CAMPAIGN TOKEN

This medal, or token as it is often referred to, was used during the 1960 Presidential election campaign by various Democratic Party groups. Originally a political item, it has now become a memorial of history and is highly sought after by collectors of Kennedy, Johnson, and general political-item collectors. The medal was issued by Special Services of Sioux Falls, South Dakota.

The obverse depicts the busts of Kennedy and Johnson and bears the inscription: "THE BEST MEN FOR THE JOB."

The head of a donkey appears in the center of the reverse together with the date "1960" and "VOTE IN NOVEMBER." Around the edge is inscribed: "PUT A DEMOCRAT BACK IN THE WHITE HOUSE/VOTE DEMOCRATIC."

This medal, issued in unlimited quantity, was struck with all edges plain.

NO.	QUANTITY	SIZE	DESCRIPTION	ORIGINAL PRICE
16	Unlimited	39mm	Goldine (goldplated)	
16-A	Unlimited	39mm	Sterling silver (edge lettered)	
16-B	Unlimited	39mm	Nickel, silver	
16-C	Unlimited	39mm	Nickel, silver, oxidized	
16-D	Unlimited	39mm	Bronze, oxidized	

INAUGURAL BALL MEDALLION

Each guest at the Inaugural Ball of January, 1961, received this small medallion. The gold-filled charms were presented to the women for use as a unit in a charm bracelet.

They were designed by Robbins Company, Attleboro, Massachusetts. These designs were later used as the basis for the medal by Executive Designs.

The obverse of this special inaugural medal bears the profile likenesses of John F. Kennedy and then Vice-President Lyndon B. Johnson facing left. There is no inscription.

The inscription on the reverse indicates that the presentation was made at the Inaugural Ball, January 20, 1961. The medal is plain edged.

Presented to the male guests for use as key chains was a like medal in base-metal silver oxidized.

NO.	QUANTITY	SIZE	DESCRIPTION	ORIGINAL PRICE
17	13,000	28mm	Gold filled, looped	Presentation piece
17-A	13,000	28mm	Silver oxidized, looped	Presentation piece

THE KENNEDY-DAY POSTMASTER MEDAL

Time Magazine issued this medal to United States postmasters who attended the National Postmaster's Convention in 1961 at Denver, Colorado.

The medals were not sold. The only source for this item is a postmaster who attended the convention.

The obverse depicts John F. Kennedy and Postmaster General J. Edward Day. It has a plain edge.

NO.	QUANTITY	SIZE	DESCRIPTION	ORIGINAL PRICE
18	1	50mm	14k gold	Presented to Day
18-A	15	50mm	Sterling silver	Presentation piece
18-B	2,500	50mm	Bronze	Presentation

31

ERIE–ETERNAL FLAME MEDAL

The Medallic Division of Erie Publishers, Buffalo, New York, issued this piece in 1965.

The medal was designed by Gerald R. Kawczynski, a professional graphic artist.

The Kennedy bust was sculptured for the original models by Mr. Kawczynski, who is also the owner of Erie Publishers.

The medal was struck by The Medal Arts Co., Inc., Rochester, New York. The company's name and address appear on the edge.

The high-relief medal has an incused field. It is a well-designed and professionally struck piece—one of the better quality pieces issued for Kennedy. It was originally sold in desk-display stand-box with a descriptive booklet.

NO.	QUANTITY	SIZE	DESCRIPTION	ORIGINAL PRICE
19	15,000	38mm	Silver, fine, .999+	$15.00
19-A	Unlimited	38mm	Bronze	5.00

KENNEDY BROTHERS NO. 1

Kennedy Coins, P.O. Box 212, Winona, Minnesota, has issued this medal as part of a set. The second piece of the set is a similar medal depicting Robert F. Kennedy, brother of John F. Kennedy.

The medals were designed by O. H. Fredriksen, National Chairman of the Robert F. Kennedy for President Clubs.

Coins in the set have a matching serial number. (See Robert Kennedy Medal, No. 21.)

NO.	QUANTITY	SIZE	DESCRIPTION	ORIGINAL PRICE
20	50,000	40mm	Bronze, silver, oxidized	$7.50

KENNEDY BROTHERS NO. 2

Robert F. Kennedy is depicted on this second of a two medal set.

The medals have been listed separately because they eventually will be separated from the set and because they are distinctively different pieces. (See No. 20.)

NO.	QUANTITY	SIZE	DESCRIPTION	ORIGINAL PRICE
21	50,000	40mm	Bronze, silver, oxidized	$7.50

COOK COUNTY MEDAL

The Democratic Party of Cook County, Illinois, presented this medal to each guest at a reception and $100-a-plate dinner held on April 28, 1961.

The medal is very scarce and is highly sought after, even now.

NO.	QUANTITY	SIZE	DESCRIPTION
22	5,000	26mm	Sterling silver, looped

PRESIDENTIAL ART CHARM

Presidential Art Medals, Inc., created a distinctive charm in 1964 and introduced the item during the American Numismatic Association Convention at Cleveland, Ohio, that same year.

The obverse of the charm is a replica of the Presidential Art Medal. Only John F. Kennedy and Lyndon B. Johnson were used in this form.

The charms as such were struck only in 14k gold and sterling silver. However, an exact bronze piece was made without the loop for embedding in lucite as a key ring.

The obverse of these three items is the same: each depicts the full face bust of Kennedy with the words "JOHN FITZ-GERALD KENNEDY" around.

The reverses are plain, except that each one is stamped in the lower area of the medal; the bronze has "MAC/NY," the silver has "MACO/NY/STERLING," and the gold has "MAC/NY/14K." The initials stand for Medallic Art Company, New York, the medalist.

The idea is good as the item makes a beautiful collection addition as well as being an ideal gift for a collector to give or receive.

34

The original announcement of these items listed them as charms and pendants in both silver and gold; however, they were the same, the only difference between the two being the inclusion on the pendant of a neck chain which is not included with the charm.

NO.	QUANTITY	SIZE	DESCRIPTION	ORIGINAL PRICE
23	Unlimited	22mm	14k gold, looped	$24.95
23-A	Unlimited	22mm	Sterling silver, looped	3.95
23-B	Unlimited	22mm	Bronze key chain	2.50

THE JOHN KENNEDY
MEMORIAL MEDAL

The above Kennedy Memorial Medal was issued by Capitol Medals, Inc., P.O. Box 667, High Point, North Carolina, in 1964. The obverse depicts a bust of Kennedy facing left, with the years of his birth and death inscribed below the chin, "1917–1963." Around the top edge is "JOHN FITZGERALD KENNEDY."

Framing the reverse is a circle of fifty stars, joined at the bottom by olive and oak branches and an eternal flame. Within the circle are the lines: " 'AND SO/FELLOW AMERICANS . . . /ASK NOT WHAT YOUR/COUNTRY CAN DO FOR YOU,/BUT ASK WHAT YOU CAN DO/FOR YOUR COUNTRY' THESE IMMORTAL WORDS FROM/OUR BELOVED 35th PRESIDENT/JOHN F. KENNEDY."

No particular designer is credited with the work; a combination of artists worked on the medal.

Struck on planchets slightly larger than a silver dollar, crown size, this medal is available in several varieties. Unlimited issues were struck in oxidized bronze and in silver oxidized bronze finishes. In addition, a restricted striking of .999 fine silver and .999 fine platinum varieties were struck. Also struck in 3-ounce Troy weight were .999 fine silver, Alphebetacones. The silver and platinum were struck in proof and serialized.

NO.	QUANTITY	SIZE	DESCRIPTION	ORIGINAL PRICE
24	25 numbered	39mm	Platinum, .999	$750.00
24-A	104 numbered	39mm	Fine silver, .999, Alphebetacones	100.00
24-B	15,000 numbered	39mm	Fine silver, .999	10.00
24-C	Unlimited	39mm	Bronze, silver, oxidized	3.50
24-D	Unlimited	39mm	Bronze, oxidized	2.50

DEMOCRATIC NATIONAL
CONVENTION TOKEN

This Kennedy piece was issued in connection with the Los Angeles Convention in 1960 and shows a kicking donkey on both sides with the inscription: "DEMOCRATIC NATIONAL CONVENTION, JULY, 1960, LOS ANGELES, CALIF."

Struck in unlimited quantities, this piece was issued with and without a ring attachment on the top.

Although originally a political item, this piece has become a memorial item and is highly sought after.

NO.	QUANTITY	SIZE	DESCRIPTION	ORIGINAL PRICE
25		40mm	Bronze, looped	
25-A		40mm	Bronze, plain	

LINCOLN-KENNEDY CENT
1964

S & S Associates, 11609 Proctor Road, Philadelphia, Pennsylvania, made and sold a 1964 Lincoln cent with the John F. Kennedy head struck on the obverse. The head is to the right of Lincoln's face.

Two varieties have been discovered. One is a plain head, and the second variety is the same head with Kennedy just above and the date, 1963, below.

This type of item, although a purely commercial venture, is medallic and was done as a tribute to Kennedy and, therefore, must be considered a part of this work. These items will become as much collector's items in the future as will the rarest medal. A collector's desire is to include all items of a series to have the feeling of completeness. This theory is borne out with experiences in other series, such as Washington and Lincoln: many years after these series began, each and every related item is still highly sought after.

The quantity struck is unknown and probably will never be established because the cents are struck in unlimited quantities until sales appeal is ended and because records are seldom kept. Approximately 2,000 have been made to date.

NO.	QUANTITY	SIZE	DESCRIPTION	ORIGINAL PRICE
26	Unlimited	.01	Plain cent	$.50
26-A	Unlimited	.01	Includes name "KENNEDY" and date "1963"	.50

1965 UNITED STATES SPOOF SET

This item is a spoof of the United States Mint officials for not striking proof sets in 1965. It is meant in the spirit of good fun.

The idea for the set was that of Joe Hylton, president of the Charganton Coin Club of La Mirada, California. Included in this set is a Kennedy piece.

The reverse bears the inscription: "COMMEMORATING/ 50¢/KENNEDY/HALF-ENOUGH/SILVER/SINCE/1965."

The balance of the 1965 United States Spoof Set is not described because none of the other tokens pertain to John F. Kennedy.

NO.	QUANTITY	DESCRIPTION	ORIGINAL PRICE
27	1,000	Sealed set of miscellaneous tokens	$1.00

PRESIDENTIAL AND
FIRST LADY MEDAL

Early in 1965, Federal Brand Enterprises of 2341 Carnegie Avenue, Cleveland, Ohio, issued this medal as a commercial venture which consisted of an entire series of Presidents and First Ladies.

This medal, although out of order for this type series, depicts and honors John F. Kennedy and Jacqueline Kennedy. The obverse shows the couple.

The reverse depicts a goddess holding a torch and a shield, standing on a globe dividing a branch of laurel. At the left is a symbol and the date "1963," above which are the words: "LIBERTY/PEACE." Below, are the initials "J. H." which are representative of Joseph Hotter, an Austrian sculptor and engraver who executed the medal.

The medal was struck in polished bronze and in silver. Only the silver pieces have been numbered.

Included with the medal is a descriptive brochure.

The entire series consists of thirty-six different pieces and are housed in the special display cases made for the medals.

There is some doubt as to the quantity struck in silver; the manufacturer, Federal Brand Enterprises, contends that only one hundred were struck. However, I have seen a specimen which was numbered two hundred.

NO.	QUANTITY	SIZE	DESCRIPTION	ORIGINAL PRICE
28	100	27mm	Silver, .900 fine	$2.50
28-A	20,000	27mm	Bronze	1.00

VINDICATION OF RIGHT
MEDAL

Charm and Treasure, Inc., of 1201 Avenue of the Americas, New York City, manufacturing jewelers, have issued this attractive charm-medal in two metals and three sizes.

The design was executed by staff employees of the company.

The piece was struck in 1964 and sold through dealers and jewelry stores. Pieces were also made into tie tacks and cufflinks.

The same company manufactured medal No. 30, a commercial venture.

NO.	QUANTITY	SIZE	DESCRIPTION	ORIGINAL PRICE
29	Unlimited	28mm	14k gold, looped	$25.00
29-A	Unlimited	27mm	14k gold, looped	19.00
29-B	Unlimited	18mm	14k gold, looped	11.00
29-C	Unlimited	28mm	14k gold, cufflinks	60.00 pair
29-D	Unlimited	28mm	14k gold, tie tacks	27.00
29-E	Unlimited	27mm	14k gold, cufflinks	47.50 pair
29-F	Unlimited	27mm	14k gold, tie tacks	20.00
29-G	Unlimited	18mm	14k gold, cufflinks	30.00 pair
29-H	Unlimited	18mm	14k gold, tie tacks	12.00
29-I	Unlimited	28mm	Silver, sterling, looped	6.00
29-J	Unlimited	27mm	Silver, sterling, looped	4.50
29-K	Unlimited	18mm	Silver, sterling, looped	3.00
29-L	Unlimited	28mm	Silver, sterling, cufflinks	15.00 pair
29-M	Unlimited	28mm	Silver, sterling, tie tack	6.50
29-N	Unlimited	27mm	Silver, sterling, cufflinks	11.00 pair
29-O	Unlimited	27mm	Silver, sterling, tie tack	5.00
29-P	Unlimited	18mm	Silver, sterling, cufflinks	8.00 pair
29-Q	Unlimited	18mm	Silver, sterling, tie tack	3.50

JFK FAMOUS QUOTATION CHARM

Charm and Treasure, Inc., 1201 Avenue of the Americas, New York City, manufacturing jewelers, have issued an attractive charm-medal in two metals and three sizes.

The obverse is somewhat different from the normal design for this type of medal. It is unusual and attractive.

The design was executed by staff employees of the company.

The piece was struck in 1964 and sold through dealers and jewelry stores.

Pieces were also made into tie tacks and cufflinks, a commercial venture.

NO.	QUANTITY	SIZE	DESCRIPTION	ORIGINAL PRICE
30	Unlimited	28mm	14k gold, looped	$25.00
30-A	Unlimited	27mm	14k gold, looped	19.00
30-B	Unlimited	18mm	14k gold, looped	11.00
30-C	Unlimited	28mm	14k gold, cufflinks	60.00 pair
30-D	Unlimited	28mm	14k gold, tie tack	27.00
30-E	Unlimited	27mm	14k gold, cufflinks	47.50 pair
30-F	Unlimited	27mm	14k gold, tie tack	20.00
30-G	Unlimited	18mm	14k gold, cufflinks	30.00 pair
30-H	Unlimited	18mm	14k gold, tie tack	12.00
30-I	Unlimited	28mm	Silver, sterling, looped	6.00
30-J	Unlimited	27mm	Silver, sterling, looped	4.50
30-K	Unlimited	18mm	Silver, sterling, looped	3.00
30-L	Unlimited	28mm	Silver, sterling, cufflinks	15.00 pair
30-M	Unlimited	28mm	Silver, sterling, tie tack	6.50
30-N	Unlimited	27mm	Silver, sterling, cufflinks	11.00 pair
30-O	Unlimited	27mm	Silver, sterling, tie tack	5.00
30-P	Unlimited	18mm	Silver, sterling, cufflinks	8.00
30-Q	Unlimited	18mm	Silver, sterling, tie tack	3.50

AETNA
VINDICATION OF RIGHT
MEDAL

This medal was manufactured by Aetna Jewelers of New York City. Although a different die was used, it is similar to No. 29. It has the jewelers mark on the reverse. The edge is plain.

NO.	QUANTITY	SIZE	DESCRIPTION	ORIGINAL PRICE
31	Unlimited	19mm	Sterling silver	$3.00

AETNA
JFK FAMOUS QUOTATION
CHARM

Aetna Jewelers of New York City manufactured these items. They were advertised as the same medal of three different sizes. However, a close examination reveals that the pieces are from different dies. Moreover, a size has been found that the company does not list. With the exception of the jewelers mark and the metal description on the reverse, these pieces are almost identical to medal No. 30 which was made by a different manufacturer. The reverses are the same. The edge is plain. Since there is a question of variety and size, only the known pieces are listed here.

Variety No. 1

Reverse, sterling

Reverse, gold

NO.	QUANTITY	SIZE	DESCRIPTION	ORIGINAL PRICE
32	Unlimited	28mm	14k gold	$25.00
32-A	Unlimited	28mm	3 variations, Sterling silver	6.00
32-B	Unlimited	24mm	2 variations, Sterling silver	4.50
32-C	Unlimited	22mm	1 variation, Sterling silver	3.00

Variety No. 2

Variety No. 3

TRIBUTE TO GREATNESS MEDAL

A. Zolnier—School Jewelers, 815 Newark Avenue, Jersey City, New Jersey, produced this medal.

The company referred to the pieces as charms and pocket coins, but this is incorrect as the producers are not medalists, and the error is a natural one.

This medal has no special significance; it is a commercial, novelty item. However, it is well done and is a quality product.

NO.	SIZE	DESCRIPTION	ORIGINAL PRICE
33	25mm	14k gold, plain	$19.95
33-A	25mm	14k gold, looped	19.95
33-B	25mm	Sterling silver, plain	5.95
33-C	25mm	Sterling silver, looped	5.95

C.C.O.A. MEDAL

B & B Supplies, 4944 Vega East, Fort Worth, Texas, began issuing a token-medal in 1962 for a worthy cause.

The above medal is the fourth in the company's yearly series of C.C.O.A. medals for the Coin Collectors of America. The medal was given free to readers of the *Numismatic News* and to customers of B & B Supplies in 1964.

C.C.O.A. is an informal organization and has no regular meetings—a meeting being defined as two or more coin collectors getting together to talk about coins. There are no dues and no formal rules.

The medal is struck in one size and one metal only.

NO.	QUANTITY	SIZE	DESCRIPTION	ORIGINAL PRICE
34	Unlimited	28mm	Aluminum	$.15

JOHN FITZGERALD KENNEDY
COMMEMORATIVE
CHARM-MEDAL

The American Charm Corporation, 48 West 48th Street, New York City, manufacturing jewelers, have made a beautiful charm-medal for President Kennedy.

The item is purely a commercial venture. However, it is one of the better-made pieces of its type and presents a good likeness of Kennedy.

The design was made by staff members of the company. Mintage is unlimited, and the quantity made is undetermined.

The items were not available for consumer sales through the manufacturer. All sales were made through dealers and jewelry stores.

45

NO.	QUANTITY	SIZE	DESCRIPTION	ORIGINAL PRICE
35	Unlimited	24mm	14k gold, yellow gold, heavy weight	$42.00
35-A	Unlimited	24mm	14k gold, yellow gold, medium weight	33.75
35-B	Unlimited	21 × 28mm	14k gold, yellow gold, oval, looped	19.50
35-C	Unlimited	24mm	Sterling silver	4.95

CUT-OUT KENNEDY HALF DOLLAR

This craft and technique is used by Bennie Klefot of Dayton, Ohio. Mr. Klefot began cutting coins in 1939. He used a jeweler's saw and fine drills and blades to accomplish this art.

Mr. Klefot has trained others in the craft but few remain active.

These pieces are beautifully done and are welcome additions to any collection. The items are made as jewelry but are seldom worn as such.

NO.	QUANTITY	SIZE	DESCRIPTION	ORIGINAL PRICE
36		Half dollar	Head and letters	$12.50
36-A		Half dollar	Head only	6.50
36-B		Half dollar	Head cut-out	2.50
36-C		15 × 23mm	Head on chain	4.50
36-D		15 × 23mm	Head tie tack	4.50
36-E		15 × 23mm	Head cufflinks	9.00

46

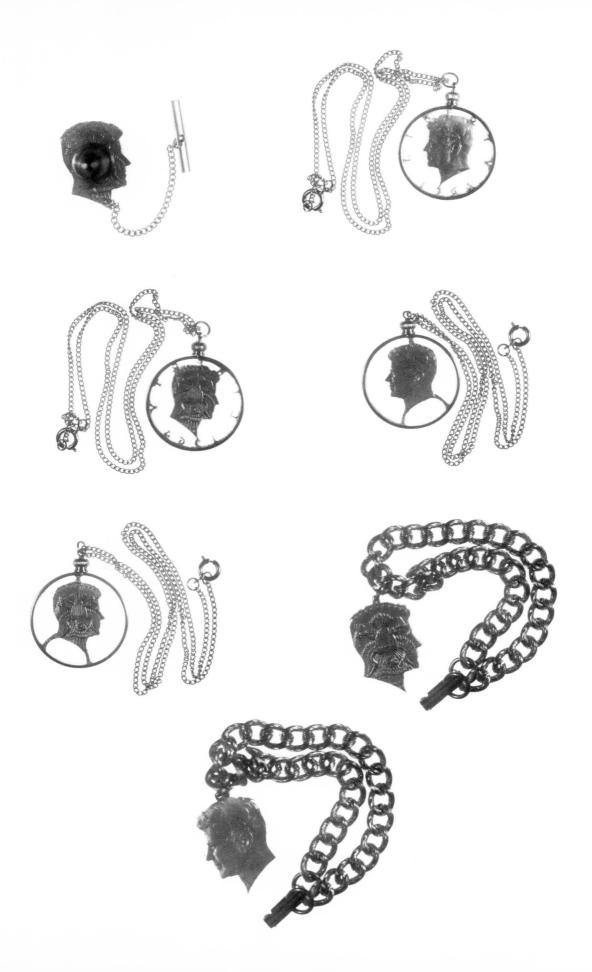

LBJ-JFK TOKEN

This medal-token is a part of a Presidential series of coins produced by the Osborne Coinage Company and sold primarily through distributors who, in turn, sell them through retail outlets. This series was sold by Hano Coins, 1598 Third Ave., New York City. The complete set sold for $10 or $1 singularly in goldine.

The obverse shows the bust of Johnson, facing left. Above is inscribed: "36th PRESIDENT, U.S.A."; below is: "LYNDON B. JOHNSON"; and to the left is: "1963."

The reverse bears seven lines of type: "LBJ/HOUSE OF REP. 1937–49/SENATE 1948–61/V. PRES. BECAME PRES./UPON DEATH OF/J. F. KENNEDY/NOV. 22, 1963." The edge is plain.

Also, this coin has been made in aluminum and used in the children's game, "Meet the Presidents," manufactured by Selchow and Righter Company. The game contains a complete set of Presidential tokens. The coin is also in rolled brass, with edges steel colored. The size is 25mm in aluminum, one of a complete set of Presidential tokens sold by Hano Coins. The complete set is sold for $3 or 25 cents singularly. All reverses and obverses are the same.

The medal-tokens were strictly commercial ventures and were manufactured in 1963 during the mourning period, which resulted in lending itself to good sales.

NO.	QUANTITY	SIZE	DESCRIPTION	ORIGINAL PRICE
37		29mm	Goldine	$1.00
37-A		29mm	Aluminum	.50
37-B		29mm	Brass, rolled steel edge	1.00
37-C		25mm	Aluminum	.25
37-D		25mm	Brass, rolled steel edge	.50

STEINBERG-KENNEDY BUST

Dr. Gerald Steinberg of Silver Spring, Maryland, designed, made the mold, and issued this unusual piece.

The pieces were made in his dental laboratory. Two pieces are known; there is only a slight difference between the two. This difference possibly occurred by using a crude mold.

These pieces are not available for purchase. The only existing pieces are in Dr. Steinberg's extensive collection of Kennedy material.

NO.	QUANTITY	SIZE	DESCRIPTION
38	1	53 × 35mm	14k gold, looped
38-A	1	53 × 35mm	Silver, plain

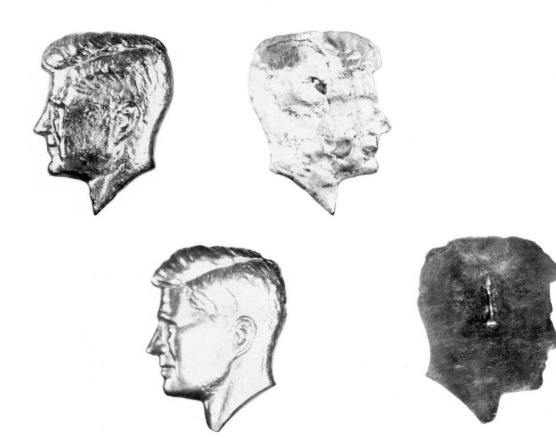

49

KENNEDY RING

One of the most unusual items in medallic art relating to John F. Kennedy is this Kennedy Ring.

The piece was designed and made by Dr. Gerald Steinberg of Silver Spring, Maryland.

The ring is not available, and this piece is in Dr. Steinberg's personal collection.

NO.	QUANTITY	SIZE	DESCRIPTION
39	Unique	32 × 22mm	14k gold

THE KENNEDYS MEDAL

Elmar Creations, 60 Tingley Street, Providence, Rhode Island, has joined the many commercial firms that made Kennedy items by issuing this charm-medal of John and Jacqueline Kennedy.

The medal is crudely made and is not particularly well designed. The process used is called "hand brocading" by the manufacturer.

The original offering of this medal was advertised in *Look Magazine* in November, 1965. Elmar Creations stated at that time that it was the sole selling agent and that the medal would not be available through retailers.

The medal was originally issued as (1) a charm on a wrist chain, (2) as a pendant with a neck chain, (3) as a key chain, and (4) as a plain token piece. Items 1 and 2 are duplicates with different chains; 3 and 4 are the same size except that 3 has a loop for the chain attachment. I have only listed the three different pieces and do not consider the various forms of original issue as distinctive pieces.

NO.	QUANTITY	SIZE	DESCRIPTION	ORIGINAL PRICE
40	Unlimited	22mm	Sterling silver, antique, looped	$4.95
40-A	Unlimited	25mm	Sterling silver, antique, looped	6.95
40-B	Unlimited	25mm	Sterling silver, antique, plain	6.95

LINCOLN-KENNEDY
WORLD'S FAIR MEDAL NO. 1

This medal was issued as a novelty and sold at the Illinois Pavilion at the 1964–65 New York World's Fair. The purpose was to raise funds to help pay for the attraction. This item was among many sold at the Pavilion and was produced by the Stafford Manufacturing Company of Brooklyn, New York.

The design supports the belief that the careers of Lincoln and Kennedy followed a similar pattern. This has been manifested in many other ways since the death of Kennedy. Among the supporters of this belief are those who were close to him.

This medal is without inscription and is holed. It is etched rather than struck on a tinlike metal.

NO.	QUANTITY	SIZE	DESCRIPTION	ORIGINAL PRICE
41	Unlimited	35mm	Holed	$1.00

LINCOLN-KENNEDY
WORLD'S FAIR MEDAL NO. 2

This medal is similar to the Lincoln-Kennedy World's Fair medal No. 1, described previously. The size and composition are the same. The portraits were changed slightly to include an inscription on the obverse and reverse. The dates "1809–1865" are above Lincoln's bust and his name appears below. The dates "1917–1963" are above Kennedy's bust, and his name is inscribed below. The medal is not holed as is the No. 1 medal.

This medal was sold at the Illinois Pavilion of the 1964–65 New York World's Fair and was presented in a plastic case.

NO.	QUANTITY	SIZE	DESCRIPTION	ORIGINAL PRICE
42	Unlimited	37mm	Inscription	$1.00

LINCOLN-KENNEDY
WORLD'S FAIR MEDAL NO. 3

This medal is of the same family as medals Nos. 41 and 42, described previously.

NO.	QUANTITY	SIZE	DESCRIPTION	ORIGINAL PRICE
43	Unlimited		Signature	$1.00

WENDALL-NORTHWESTERN MEMORIAL MEDAL

In 1964, Wendall-Northwestern, Inc., 2414 Franklin Ave., Minneapolis, Minnesota, struck this medal as a memorial medal, but did so purely as a commercial venture.

NO.	QUANTITY	SIZE	DESCRIPTION	ORIGINAL PRICE
44		37mm	Sterling silver	$5.00
44-A		37mm	Bronze, antique	1.50

JFK-WHITE HOUSE MEDAL

This medal was struck as a souvenir for sale in novelty stores and is found mainly in New York City. It was struck and sold by a novelty company in Providence, Rhode Island. It has a reeded edge and is looped.

Like many items of this nature, it is difficult to determine the quantity issued. The design, although attractive, is very crudely manufactured. This is not unusual for give-away-type pieces. The originals were key rings.

They were issued in one size only and of one metal but each has a different finish.

NO.	QUANTITY	SIZE	DESCRIPTION	ORIGINAL PRICE
45		36mm	Zinc, gilt	$1.00
45-A		36mm	Zinc, silvered	1.00
45-B		36mm	Zinc, silvered, antique	1.00
45-C		36mm	Zinc, bronzed	1.00

KENNEDY FAMILY CHARMS

This item should appear in the novel, miscellaneous group, but it was decided to give it a separate listing because it is an unusual piece and is most interesting.

The individual charms depict the President, his wife, and their two children.

The reverse is a plain ray effect.

The item was manufactured in 1964 by an unknown novelty company and sold primarily in the New York City area.

The quantity made is questionable since these ventures were quite unsuccessful and any unsold stock was destroyed.

The charms are of a gold and bronze color coated on a zinc-like metal.

NO.	QUANTITY	SIZE	DESCRIPTION	ORIGINAL PRICE
46		22mm	Gilded	$1.00
46-A		22mm	Bronzed	1.00

SCULPTURED COIN

Sculptured Coins, Inc., a private organization located in New York City, has used an old craft and process to make this unusual piece.

A Kennedy Half Dollar is used to produce the detail and bustlike head of President Kennedy. These items are made under tremendous pressures from specially prepared dies.

The originator of the process is unknown, but it was patented on August 11, 1903, and soon after, this type of item began to appear for sale. At first, the pieces were manufactured from half dollars, quarters, nickels, and dimes.

The government banned the manufacture at the time because of a law relative to the mutilation of silver coins. The present law applies only to alteration or mutilation for fraudulent purposes.

No special dates are used for the pieces; rather, they are made from coins bought on the open market and the date has no bearing on the item.

NO.	QUANTITY	SIZE	DESCRIPTION	ORIGINAL PRICE
47	Unlimited	$.50	Kennedy Half Dollar	$5.00

LUCKY PENNY NO. 1

"Memorial Highway"

Unidentified as to maker and origin.

NO.	QUANTITY	SIZE	DESCRIPTION	ORIGINAL PRICE
48		34 × 39mm	Aluminum horseshoe	$1.00

LUCKY PENNY NO. 2

"In Memoriam"

Issued by Earl Fankhauser of Fort Wayne, Indiana. Mr. Fankhauser's name and Fort Wayne appear in small letters on the reverse.

NO.	QUANTITY	SIZE	DESCRIPTION	ORIGINAL PRICE
49		32mm	Aluminum ring	$1.00

LUCKY PENNY NO. 3

"Kennedy-Johnson"

This is the same as No. 49, described previously, in that it was issued by Earl Fankhauser.

NO.	QUANTITY	SIZE	DESCRIPTION	ORIGINAL PRICE
50		32mm	Aluminum ring	$1.00

LUCKY PLAQUE

Normally, this piece would not be included in a medal collection; however, we accept this piece because it is medallic art of a higher form. During the period shortly after President Kennedy's death, hundreds of novel busts and plaques were made and sold to souvenir collectors.

Masterpieces in Bronze, a division of Acrometal Products, Inc., 616 N. 5th Street, Minneapolis, Minnesota, designed this hand-crafted plaque at the request of schools, businesses, and institutions which wanted a worthy memorial of President Kennedy. The item became very popular and, as a result of individual requests for the plaque, the company decided to make a limited number of these pieces available to the public.

Seven hundred and fifty registered copies were produced and numbered in serial. It is sculptured in burnished copper. The quality is good, and the artist, an employee of the company, created the original in detail and the familiar face of John F. Kennedy, which appears very young in this work, is set in high relief against a black background. The plaque is mounted in a solid walnut frame.

NO.	QUANTITY	SIZE	DESCRIPTION	ORIGINAL PRICE
51	750	18½ × 22½ inches	Copper, black field, walnut frame	$19.95

JOHN F. KENNEDY
ELONGATED CENTS

"I"   "II"   "III"

As with most subjects struck in metal, some person, firm, or group will imprint what we know as elongated cents. This process is a very old one and has been a continuous practice for many years.

The cents shown above were made by Mr. Ralph Jones, 3048 North Third Street, Philadelphia, Pennsylvania. Jones did not use cents of the current year, but cents of various dates. This resulted in each and every date being of a variety. This was not intentional, but a convenience. It was much easier to buy a bag of cents and use these rather than pick out dates of one particular year.

In 1954, Ralph Jones was a collector of elongated cents specializing in Columbian Exposition, including all related items. The cents he collected were plain and crudely prepared. Because he is a true collector and recognized the value in elongated cents to a collector as well as the potential in this type of item for a series, he decided to manufacture these cents and interest other collectors in them.

On September 25, 1963, Jones bought for $150 his first machine to make these cents. It was a hand-crank model from which he made 350 pieces. His customers liked the cents he produced, and his business grew. He then built a motor for this machine and increased his production.

58

The first items Jones produced were a store card for himself, the John F. Kennedy Assassination Cent No. 5, and a Civil War Centennial piece.

Jones has since made many different elongated cents depicting a number of subjects. Those relating to Kennedy are the Kennedy Assassination, No. 5 and the Kennedy Visit to Independence Hall in Philadelphia in 1962, No. 3.

NO.	QUANTITY	SIZE	DESCRIPTION	ORIGINAL PRICE
52		Cent	In memoriam	$.50
53		Cent	Assassination	.50
54		Cent	Independence Hall	.50

ADDITIONAL
ELONGATED CENTS

4
USA T-2

1
Cameo

2
Terminal

3
USA T-1

5
USA T-3

NO.	QUANTITY	SIZE	DESCRIPTION	ORIGINAL PRICE
55			Cameo	$.50
56			Terminal	.50
57			USA T-1	.50
58			USA T-2	.50
59			USA T-3	.50

OSBORNE TOKEN SERIES

The Osborne Company of Cincinnati, Ohio, produces this series of John F. Kennedy biographical tokens. The items are sold by various firms.

The tokens are also used in children's games; these are usually the aluminum variety.

No. 60, 28mm, goldine
>The obverse of this piece shows the bust of Kennedy facing left with the inscription: "35th PRESIDENT, U.S.A." above and "JOHN F. KENNEDY" below. "1961" is to the left; "1963" is to the right. The reverse is inscribed with "JFK" at the top and around the bottom is "HARVARD GRADUATE/NAVY 1941–1945/CONGRESS 1947–1953/SENATE 1953–1961/PULITZER PRIZE AUTHOR 1957."

No. 61, 28mm, goldine
>The obverse of this piece is the same as No. 60. The reverse displays the inscription "JFK" at the top and "CONGRESS 1947–1953/SENATE 1953–1961/ASSASSINATED/NOV. 22, 1963/ORIGINATOR OF PEACE CORPS" around the bottom.

No. 61-A
>Same as No. 61 in nickel.

No. 62, 28mm, goldine
>The obverse of this token is the same as No. 60, with the exception that the bust is smaller. The reverse is the same as No. 61.

No. 62-A, 25mm, aluminum
>The obverse and reverse are identical to No. 62.

No. 63, 28mm, goldine
>The obverse is the same as No. 60 but without "1963" inscribed to the right. The reverse is inscribed with the words "JFK" at the top and around the bottom is "HARVARD GRADUATE/NAVY 1941–1945/CONGRESS 1947–1953/SENATE 1953–1961/INAUGURAL JAN. 20th, 1961."

No. 63-A
>Same as No. 63 in nickel.

No. 64, 28mm, goldine

The obverse is the same as No. 63. The reverse bears the inscription "JACK" at the top and around the bottom "HARVARD GRADUATE/NAVY 1941–1945/CONGRESS 1947–1953/SENATE 1953–1961/PULITZER PRIZE AUTHOR 1957."

No. 65, 28mm, goldine, looped

The obverse is the same as No. 63. The reverse is inscribed, in script, "BEST WISHES/JOHN KENNEDY."

No. 66

The obverse and reverse of this token are the same as No. 64, with the exception that "JFK" appears on the reverse instead of "JACK."

No. 67, 28mm, goldine

The obverse is the same as No. 63. The reverse depicts the White House in the center, with the words "THE WHITE HOUSE" around the top. "INAUGURATED" appears under the White House, and "JANUARY 20, 1961," is around the bottom.

No. 68, 28mm, goldine

This is looped and has a donkey attached. The obverse is the same as No. 63. The reverse depicts the Capitol Building with the words "UNITED STATES CAPITOL" around the top.

No. 69, 28mm, goldine, looped

The obverse is the same as No. 63. The reverse depicts the White House, with the words "THE WHITE HOUSE" around the bottom.

The series will have to settle, and this collector will have to become more familiar with the Osborne pieces before he can determine exactly how many pieces there are and can list the many varieties.

MANSHIP-COPY MEDAL

I have so titled this medal simply because the bust is identical to the Manship original.

Information received from the seller stated that the medal was designed by Luigi Morini and struck by Harvey Klitznec, Inc., of Providence, Rhode Island.

This medal was issued immediately after the assassination of Kennedy.

Each of the obverses shown here is slightly different, with the exception of varieties 3 and 4, the only difference here being that 3 is not looped. The reverses of 1 and 4 are the same except for the sterling mark on 1. A smooth field is on the reverse of 3, and 1 and 4 have a textured field.

NO.	QUANTITY	SIZE	DESCRIPTION	ORIGINAL PRICE
70		29mm	1. Sterling silver, antique	$2.50
70-A		29mm	2. Sterling silver	2.50
70-B		29mm	3. Bronze	1.00
70-C		29mm	4. Bronze, looped	1.00
70-D		29mm	5. Zinc, gilt, looped	1.00

"ASK NOT"-TORCH MEDAL

This medal is relatively unknown. It was sold through a stamp company in Philadelphia, Pennsylvania. The only information available is that the piece was struck in Chicago.

It is an attractive medal and is similar to many others in the John F. Kennedy series.

NO.	QUANTITY	SIZE	DESCRIPTION	ORIGINAL PRICE
71		39mm	Goldplated	
71-A		39mm	Silver, oxidized	

PRESIDENT AND VICE-PRESIDENT INAUGURATION MEDAL

The obverse depicts the Capitol Building. There is a flowing ribbon to the right and left with the names "KENNEDY" on the left ribbon and "JOHNSON" on the right ribbon. Just below the Capitol is an eagle behind a shield of stars and stripes. Fifty stars make up the field around and above the Capitol dome. Around the outside is "INAUGURATION OF/PRESIDENT AND/VICE PRESIDENT."

NO.	QUANTITY	SIZE	DESCRIPTION	ORIGINAL PRICE
72		42mm	Bronze	

35TH PRESIDENT CHARM

Beaucraft, Inc., of Providence, Rhode Island, made this charm. It is found in most jewelry stores. It has a plain edge, looped.

NO.	QUANTITY	SIZE	DESCRIPTION	ORIGINAL PRICE
73		12 × 15mm	Sterling silver	$1.00

BOSTON MARCHING GROUP INAUGURAL PARADE MEDAL

This highly sought-after medal was made on behalf of the Ancient and Honorable Artillery Company of Massachusetts, a marching group that participated in the inaugural parade for President Kennedy on January 20, 1961. The medals were made in sets of two: the regular issue and a smaller copy. Both had a blue and white ribbon.

With the exception of special issues to certain people, only the members of the marching group received the medal. Of the regular issue, an additional set was made for the Military Museum in Boston.

The obverse depicts a left-facing bust of Kennedy which is a copy of the Manship Medal No. 11. Around the outside appears "ANCIENT AND HONORABLE ARTILLERY CO./1638 MASSACHUSETTS 1961." In the inside circle around the bust is "JOHN FITZGERALD KENNEDY/ PRESIDENT OF THE/UNITED STATES OF/AMER-ICA." On the reverse is "I. JEROME O'CONNER/CAP-TAIN COMMANDING/THIS MEDAL/LIMITED TO 75/ COPIES ONLY/PRESENTED TO: [blank center for name of recipient and number of medal]. INAUGURAL PARADE/ WASHINGTON, D.C./20 JANUARY 1961." The dies were destroyed.

64

NO.	QUANTITY	SIZE	DESCRIPTION	ORIGINAL PRICE
74	Unique	38mm	Gold	Presented to Kennedy
74-A	Unique	20mm	Gold	
74-B	76	38mm	Silver	
74-C	76	20mm	Silver	
74-D	2	38mm	Sterling	No. 1 John Volpe, Massachusetts governor No. 2 John F. Collins, Boston mayor
74-E	2	20mm	Sterling	As above

KENNEDY–"ASK NOT" CHARM

Similar to many other bust charms, this piece was issued by the Fort Jewelry Company of Rhode Island. Scarce now, this was distributed in many stores in the larger cities.

The obverse has a left-facing bust of Kennedy and a proof surface. The reverse reads "ASK NOT/WHAT YOUR COUNTRY/CAN DO FOR YOU—/ASK WHAT YOU/CAN DO FOR/YOUR COUNTRY." The words "JOHN F. KENNEDY/1917–1963" appear below, with "STERLING AND 'F' " in a circle.

NO.	QUANTITY	SIZE	DESCRIPTION	ORIGINAL PRICE
75		13 × 15mm	Sterling	$1.50

KENNEDY-DAWN CHARM

Dawn Creations of Providence, Rhode Island, manufactured this item. It is suspected, because of similarity in many other items, that this company has made other Kennedy items such as tie tacks and miscellaneous jewelry.

The obverse has a Kennedy bust outlined, facing left. The reverse reads "ASK NOT/WHAT YOUR COUNTRY/CAN DO FOR YOU—/ASK WHAT YOU/CAN DO FOR/YOUR COUNTRY/JOHN F. KENNEDY [in script] 1917–1963 [below] STERLING 'AL' '' in a circle. This medal is identified with Dawn Creations; however, the manufacturer is questionable. It has a plain edge, looped.

NO.	QUANTITY	SIZE	DESCRIPTION	ORIGINAL PRICE
76		12 × 16mm	Sterling	$1.50

ELONGATED UNITED STATES COIN MEMORIALS

Ralph Jones of Philadelphia, who is referred to and described on page 58, has added to his elongated cents business the issuing of his Kennedy die designs on the United States nickel through the dollar.

The law covering the defacing of United States currency is interpreted as defacing for fraudulent purposes. The items, as other types, would not come under the law.

Less than one hundred of each set were made.

Type 1

NO.	QUANTITY	SIZE	DESCRIPTION	ORIGINAL PRICE
77		$ .05	Type 1	$.05, .10, .25
77-A		.10	Type 1	5.00, set
77-B		.25	Type 1	
77-C		.50	Type 1	3.50
77-D		1.00	Type 1	5.00
77-E		.05	Type 2	.05, .10, .25
77-F		.10	Type 2	5.00, set
77-G		.25	Type 2	
77-H		.50	Type 2	3.50
77-I		1.00	Type 2	5.00
77-J		.05	Type 3	.05, .10, .25
77-K		.10	Type 3	5.00, set
77-L		.25	Type 3	
77-M		.50	Type 3	3.50
77-N		1.00	Type 3	5.00

Type 2

Type 3

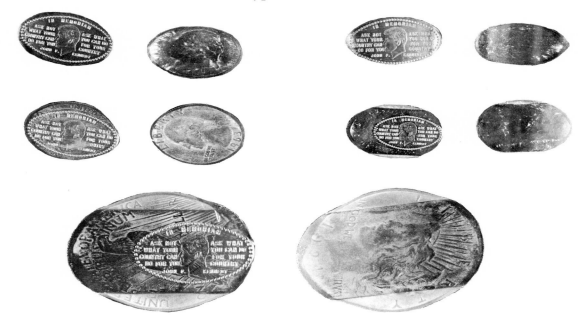

PROFILE IN COURAGE MEDAL

This medal was designed by Charles Naimot of New York City. The designer made only one copy and presented it to Jacqueline Kennedy. The medal was made in 1964.

NO.	QUANTITY	SIZE
78	Unique	38mm

MEN IN SPACE MEDAL

NO.	QUANTITY	SIZE	DESCRIPTION	ORIGINAL PRICE
79			Silvered	$1.00

68

WHITE HOUSE–D.C. MEDAL

This medal is similar to No. 45, except that it does not have terminal dates nor is it looped.

The medal is crudely made with a reeded edge.

NO.	DESCRIPTION	ORIGINAL PRICE
80	Goldine	$1.00

MISCELLANEOUS CHARMS

These charm items, issued as commercial products, were sold generally in the New York City area.

NO.	QUAN-TITY	SIZE	DESCRIPTION	ORIGINAL PRICE
81			No. 1, Kennedy in chair, sterling	$3.00
82		15 × 18mm	No. 2, Bust, sterling	3.50
83		13 × 5mm	No. 4, Rocking chair, sterling	3.50
84		15 × 13mm	No. 5, Enameled, blue and white	1.00
85		14 × 12mm	No. 6, Enameled, concave	1.00

MISCELLANEOUS CHARMS

NO.	QUAN-TITY	SIZE	DESCRIPTION	ORIGINAL PRICE
86		21mm	No. 7, Proof rim, matte surface	2.50
87		21mm	No. 8, Proof rim, 12k gold	7.95
88		21mm	No. 9, Proof rim, No. 2, 12k gold	7.95
89		25mm	No. 10, Wide rim, 14k gold	9.95
90			No. 11, Enameled, 14k gold	
91		31mm	No. 12, 1961 Capitol	1.00
92		23mm	No. 13, JFK plain	1.00

6

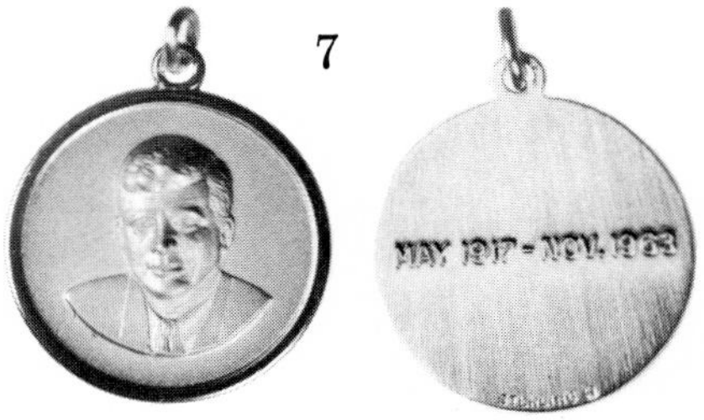

7

8

9

10

11

12

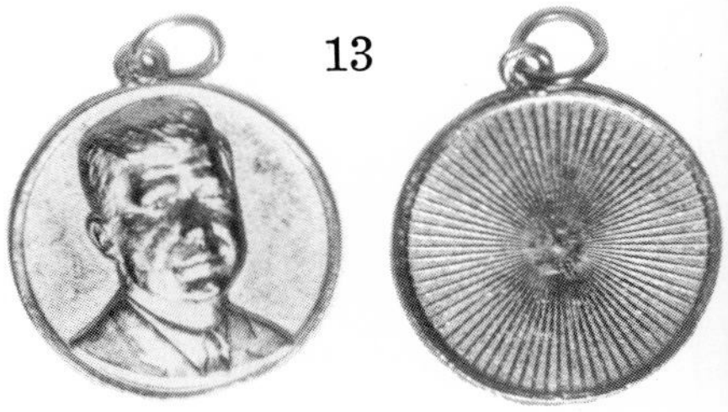

13

MISCELLANEOUS KEY RINGS

Normally, these items would have an individual listing because they are distinctive in themselves. However, they were acquired at the last moment and proper research was not possible. Therefore, I have listed them as key rings simply to display. The numbers are permanent. Number 6 is made in Germany.

1

NO.	QUAN-TITY	SIZE	DESCRIPTION	ORIGINAL PRICE
93		43mm	No. 1, P.A.M., gold plated	$3.50
94		31mm	No. 2, Enameled, Germany	5.00
95		23mm	No. 3, Goldine	1.50
		25 × 10mm	Tag	
96		30mm	No. 4, Plain ring	1.00
		32 × 10mm	Tag	
97		31 × 10mm	No. 5, Tag, half	1.50

3

4

2

5

MISCELLANEOUS KEY RINGS

NO.	QUAN-TITY	SIZE	DESCRIPTION	ORIGINAL PRICE
98		32mm	No. 6, Bust, cut-out, silver	2.50
99		20 × 15mm	No. 7, Chair, gilt	
		26mm	Tag	1.50
100		25 × 15mm	No. 8, Bust, goldplated	2.50
		25mm	Tag	
101		22mm	Nos. 9, 17, 63, silvered	1.50
102		35mm	No. 10, Memoriam, gilt	1.00
103			No. 11, Case	2.00

6

7

8

9

10

11

MISCELLANEOUS
KENNEDY PLAQUES

No. 1, embossed metal sheet on wooden plaque
   104, enameled, gilt finish

No. 2, bubble-hollow wall plaque, reverse plain
   105, polished bronze

No. 3, made like an identification card, gilt
   106, printed design

No. 4, cast, painted center, black, high relief
   107 bust

1

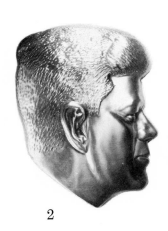

2

4

3

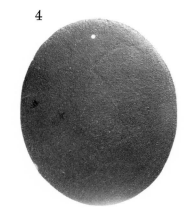

1

2

3

MISCELLANEOUS "ASK NOT" SERIES

The medals depicted here are of unknown origin, and it was decided, therefore, to group all medals of this nature and unknown origin. In subsequent writings, individual listings will be made as new information is acquired. These items will be numbered for reference purposes, and the numbers given will remain their permanent identification.

These were struck or manufactured and distributed through novelty stores in various quantities. However, it is estimated that the quantity was small since items of this nature were very unpopular and, therefore, had little financial return for the company that sold them. These items were in the form of key rings, tokens, bracelets, necklace pieces, etc. A further search and study of them may reveal more information, such as metals, quantity, and makers.

In contacting a number of firms that venture into the production of this type of novelty, it was revealed that they were very unhappy with the results. Many of these people stated that they issued minimum quantities as a feeler for sales and, in most cases, immediately discontinued further manufacture.

These particular medals vary in quality and workmanship. The metals are commercial alloys.

It is estimated that less than one thousand each of these were made. Since their publication in the early part of 1964, they have completely disappeared from the market.

A close study of these items will reveal a number of varieties of the same die or design. In a few cases, the same portrait of Kennedy was used; the medals have varying designs and portrait size but are otherwise identical.

It has been noted on other medals that manufacturers simply take a design with little regard to origin or ownership and reproduce it to their specifications. Apparently, this was done in many cases from foreign designs.

A continued study will be made of these items. Additional information will be documented and recorded for future publication.

4

5

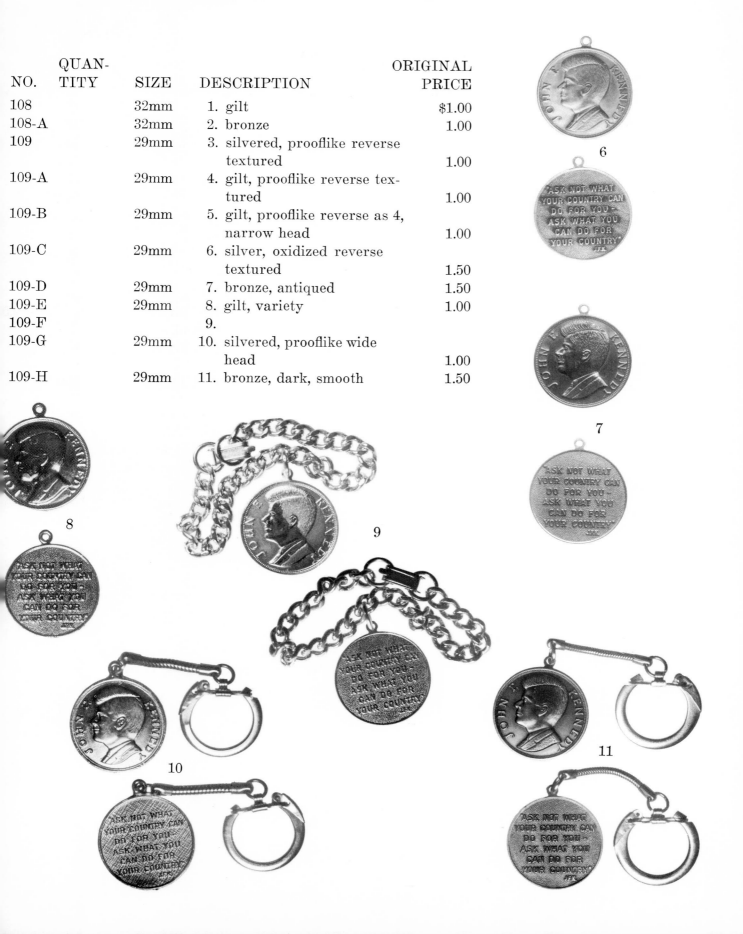

NO.	QUAN-TITY	SIZE	DESCRIPTION	ORIGINAL PRICE
108		32mm	1. gilt	$1.00
108-A		32mm	2. bronze	1.00
109		29mm	3. silvered, prooflike reverse textured	1.00
109-A		29mm	4. gilt, prooflike reverse textured	1.00
109-B		29mm	5. gilt, prooflike reverse as 4, narrow head	1.00
109-C		29mm	6. silver, oxidized reverse textured	1.50
109-D		29mm	7. bronze, antiqued	1.50
109-E		29mm	8. gilt, variety	1.00
109-F			9.	
109-G		29mm	10. silvered, prooflike wide head	1.00
109-H		29mm	11. bronze, dark, smooth	1.50

6

7

8

9

10

11

MISCELLANEOUS
"ASK NOT" SERIES

NO.	QUAN-TITY	SIZE	DESCRIPTION	ORIGINAL PRICE
109-I		29mm	12. silvered, wide head variety	1.00
109-J		29mm	13. silver, oxidized, smooth	1.50
110		28mm	14. gilt, copy of Aetna Jewelers	1.00
110-A		28mm	15. silvered, same as 14	1.00
111		31mm	16. smooth, silvered, antique	
112		28mm	17. bronze, looped	
112-A		28mm	18. bronze, plain	
113			19. cast, bronzed, copied from Manship Medal	2.50
114		33mm	20. gilt, proof head, matte field, smooth revision	2.50
115		34mm	21. goldine	1.50
116		35mm	22. silver oxidized	1.50
117		30mm	23. base-metal	1.00

12

13

14

25

MISCELLANEOUS
"ASK NOT" SERIES

NO.	QUAN-TITY	SIZE	DESCRIPTION	ORIGINAL PRICE
118		65mm	24. gilt, cast Manship bust	3.00
118-A		65mm	Silvered, cast	2.50
118-B		65mm	Bronzed, cast	2.00
119		30mm	25. silvered, smooth	1.00
120		22mm	26. silver oxidized	3.50
121		32mm	27. silvered, antique	1.50
122		29mm	28. bronze, obverse textured, reverse smooth	1.50
123		27mm	29. gilt, reverse concave	1.00
124		39mm, tag 25 × 14mm	30. rim and tag, black paint field	

24

26

28

27

29

30

MISCELLANEOUS
JEWELRY ITEMS

These assorted jewelry items were made for commercial purposes by various jewelry firms in New York City.

NO.	QUAN-TITY	SIZE	DESCRIPTION	ORIGINAL PRICE
125		22mm	1. brooch, gilt	$2.50
126		16mm	2. tie tack, bronzed	1.00
127		22mm	3. cufflink, silvered	1.00
128		22mm	4. tie clasp, silvered	1.00
129		22mm	5. cufflink, gilt	1.00
130			6. bracelet, gilt	2.50
131		33 × 35mm	7. heart charm	1.50

8

132	23mm	8. cufflink, silvered	1.00
133	22mm	9. artcraft medal, gilt	1.50
134	24 × 15mm	10. bust charm, bronze, antique	1.50
135		11. tie clasp, bronzed	1.00
135-A		tie clasp, silvered	1.00
135-B		12. tie clasp, gilt	1.00
136		13. tie clasp, 109, gilt	1.00
137		14. cufflinks, silvered	1.00
138		15. tie clasp, K-60, gilt	1.00
139	16mm	16. tie tack, gilt	.50
140		17. capitol charm bracelet	1.50
141	29mm	18. watch charm	8.50
142		19. gilt, tie tack	.50
142-A		Silvered	.50
142-B		Bronzed	.50
143		20. gilt, tie tack	.25

9

11

12

13

10

KENNEDY-WHISKEYTOWN MEDAL

The Redding, California, Chamber of Commerce issued this medal to commemorate the Kennedy-Whiskeytown Memorial in memory of Kennedy's visit for the dedication of the Whiskeytown Dam in 1963. The obverse shows a steel memorial with six plaques sculptured by Robert Ciabani. Each plaque shows an interest of Kennedy. Whiskeytown Lake is in the background. The plaques designate "PEACE CORPS: CIVIL RIGHTS: NATURAL RESOURCES: DEFENSE OF LIBERTY: 35TH PRESIDENT." Below is "JOHN F. KENNEDY/1919–1963" (birthdate in error). Around the outside is "19 KENNEDY-WHISKEYTOWN MEMORIAL 65/REDDING-SHASTA COUNTY CALIFORNIA."

The reverse depicts a miner panning for gold. Around the top is "100 YEARS FROM MINING TO RECREATION" and below is "SOUVENIR GOLD COIN." Below the miner is "MINING 1862." Three circles each have the words: "BRANDY CREEK, FRENCH GULCH, WHISKEY-TOWN." It has a plain edge.

NO.	QUANTITY	SIZE	DESCRIPTION	ORIGINAL PRICE
144		39mm	Nickel, silver, unnumbered	
144-A	300	39mm	Nickel, silver, numbered	
144-B	5,000	39mm	Goldine	

NTA PRESENTATION MEDAL

Senator Edward Kennedy accepted this medal from the Northern Textile Association for President Kennedy.

Designed and struck by the Medallic Art Company of New York City, the obverse shows a head of a sheep to represent wool on the right; cotton balls appear on the left; and machinery is in the center to denote the synthetic textiles. In the background is a loom and the letters "NTA" on a piece of cloth. Around the rim is a border of cotton hanks. Around the top is "NORTHERN TEXTILE ASSOCIATION" and below is "FOUNDED 1854."

The reverse is a plain field with "JOHN F. KENNEDY" engraved in the center, circled by a wreath with a spread eagle at the bottom. The ribbon at the feet of the eagle has "A.D. 1899" on it. It has a plain edge.

NO.	QUANTITY	SIZE	DESCRIPTION
145	Unique	64mm	Gold

JOHN F. KENNEDY LIFE AND ACHIEVEMENT SERIES

Vanguard Medals of New York City planned, designed and are issuing this series—a new medal series unlike anything offered before to the collector of Kennedy medallic art. The series is unique, and a complete set of all medals represents a complete history of John F. Kennedy.

The obverse remains the same with a changing reverse depicting highlights in detail of the life and achievements of our late President from birth to death.

The medals are beautifully designed and struck in high relief. Edges are numbered consecutively, one to one thousand.

Dies will be retired permanently after each issue of one thousand is struck.

The series is offered by membership only. The charter membership was $10.00, plus $10.00 per silver medal issued, plus $10.00 for a case to house the entire set; the total cost to each member for the complete package was $270.00. At the time of original issue a special offer was made to anyone who wanted to pay the full cost in advance. That price was $200.00.

One hundred sets were duplicated in 14 carat gold and issued for presentation and sale.

NO.	QUANTITY	SIZE	DESCRIPTION	ORIGINAL PRICE
146	100	50mm	Gold 14k-Birth	$500.00
146-A	1,000	50mm	Silver .999-Birth	10.00
147	100	50mm	Gold 14k-Confirmation	500.00
147-A	1,000	50mm	Silver .999-Confirmation	10.00
148	100	50mm	Gold 14k-High School	500.00
148-A	1,000	50mm	Silver .999-High School	10.00
149	100	50mm	Gold 14k-Harvard	500.00
149-A	1,000	50mm	Silver .999-Harvard	10.00
150	100	50mm	Gold 14k-Naval Service	500.00
150-A	1,000	50mm	Silver .999-Naval Service	10.00
151	100	50mm	Gold 14k	500.00
151-A	1,000	50mm	Silver .999	10.00
152	100	50mm	Gold 14k	500.00
152-A	1,000	50mm	Silver .999	10.00
153	100	50mm	Gold 14k	500.00
153-A	1,000	50mm	Silver .999	10.00
154	100	50mm	Gold 14k	500.00
154-A	1,000	50mm	Silver .999	10.00
155	100	50mm	Gold 14k	500.00
155-A	1,000	50mm	Silver .999	10.00
156	100	50mm	Gold 14k	500.00
156-A	1,000	50mm	Silver .999	10.00
157	100	50mm	Gold 14k	500.00
157-A	1,000	50mm	Silver .999	10.00
158	100	50mm	Gold 14k	500.00
158-A	1,000	50mm	Silver .999	10.00

NO.	QUANTITY	SIZE	DESCRIPTION	ORIGINAL PRICE
159	100	50mm	Gold 14k	500.00
159-A	1,000	50mm	Silver .999	10.00
160	100	50mm	Gold 14k	500.00
160-A	1,000	50mm	Silver .999	10.00
161	100	50mm	Gold 14k	500.00
161-A	1,000	50mm	Silver .999	10.00
162	100	50mm	Gold 14k	500.00
162-A	1,000	50mm	Silver .999	10.00
163	100	50mm	Gold 14k	500.00
163-A	1,000	50mm	Silver .999	10.00
164	100	50mm	Gold 14k	500.00
164-A	1,000	50mm	Silver .999	10.00
165	100	50mm	Gold 14k	500.00
165-A	1,000	50mm	Silver .999	10.00
166	100	50mm	Gold 14k	500.00
166-A	1,000	50mm	Silver .999	10.00
167	100	50mm	Gold 14k	500.00
167-A	1,000	50mm	Silver .999	10.00
168	100	50mm	Gold 14k	500.00
168-A	1,000	50mm	Silver .999	10.00
169	100	50mm	Gold 14k-Assassination	500.00
169-A	1,000	50mm	Silver .999-Assassination	10.00

KENNEDY-HOWDEN MEDAL

Do Howden of Beverly Hills, California, designed and issued this piece. The obverse shows a front face of Kennedy with a wreath around outside. "1917–1963" is at the bottom. The reverse shows a dove, head down, with wings spread and holding a branch in his beak. Both surfaces are textured. It is looped.

NO.	QUANTITY	SIZE	DESCRIPTION	ORIGINAL PRICE
170		32mm	Zinc	

JANON "ASK NOT" MEDAL

This medal is the original of a medal that has been widely copied by novelty firms as looped key rings in various metals. This piece is struck only in bronze and is limited to seven hundred fifty pieces.

This is a scarce Kennedy item. Obverse is smooth antique bronze. Reverse is textured antique. Plain edge.

Janon, a mail-order house in New York City, discovered the dies with B & R Associates of New York City. An unknown person from Chicago had ordered the dies made but never placed an order for the striking. Janon asked B & R if they had struck from the dies and they stated they had not. An order was placed with the company for a limited striking of seven hundred fifty pieces with a guarantee that no additional pieces would be struck in the future. The issue was sold only through Coin World. The actual striking was done by Union Tool and Die Works of Providence, Rhode Island.

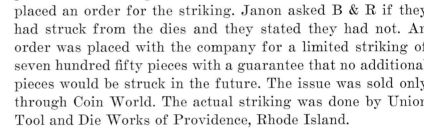

NO.	QUANTITY	SIZE	DESCRIPTION	ORIGINAL PRICE
171	750	29mm	Bronze, antique	$2.50

ASSASSINATION OF JOHN F. KENNEDY MEDAL

This medal of the assassination of President John F. Kennedy depicts the President on the obverse and Lee Harvey Oswald and Jack Ruby on the reverse in beautiful medallic art. The medal is unusual in design and workmanship.

Vanguard Medals of New York City issued the medal and it was struck by Union Tool and Die Works of Providence, Rhode Island. The medal was created and designed by Andrew Faller and Aubrey Mayhew.

86

Gold and silver pieces are numbered on the edge. (The lead die trial was used for the photograph since striking had not begun at publication.)

NO.	QUANTITY	SIZE	DESCRIPTION	ORIGINAL PRICE
172	25	38mm	Gold 14k	$350.00
172-A	1,000	38mm	Silver .999	10.00
172-B		38mm	Bronze, antique	3.00
172-C	1	36mm	Die trial-obv. lead	

HATFIELD-KENNEDY MEDAL

In September, 1964, Mr. M. J. Hatfield of Newton, Connecticut, a semi-retired tool and die maker, modeled, molded and cast this medal for a pastime. He did not plan a large issue or wide distribution. In fact, he cast the metal in small lots and sold them at carnivals, church bazaars and door-to-door only in the immediate area of Newton. The initial casting and sale consisted of approximately one hundred pieces.

Mr. Hatfield attempted to copyright the medal. On the first piece or mold was a small circled ''R'' for copyright purposes on the lower left hand rim, and his initials, M.J.H., in the same position on the right side. He could not register the piece, so he removed the copyright notice and cast an additional one hundred pieces.

Soon after the second group was cast, Mr. Hatfield noticed the inscription on the reverse read: "ASK NOT WHAT YOUR COUNTRY WILL DO FOR YOU—ASK WHAT YOU CAN DO FOR YOUR COUNTRY." This of course was incorrect, so he changed the same mold again. The word WILL was changed to CAN. Since he was re-working the mold, he decided to spell his name out, and the M.J.H. on the lower right side became M. J. Hatfield. Therefore there were three types of original medal. There were approximately eight hundred of the third type cast.

The medals were cast in white metal composed of lead, antimony and tin. Type one was chrome-plated, types two and three were sprayed with a lacquer paint in three different colors: gold, silver and copper. The medal was originally made as a paperweight and weighed 5⅓ ounces. The idea was set aside by Mr. Hatfield soon afterward and the project forgotten until Mr. Angelo A. Rosato, of New Milford, Connecticut, a jeweler by trade and collector by hobby, happened to see one of the pieces in a junk shop in Newton, Connecticut. He bought the medal, noticed Mr. Hatfield's name inscribed and went about locating him. Mr. Rosato found Mr. Hatfield, and got his consent to re-issue the medal; he, Mr. Rosato, acting as the distributor. This was not an easy task, since Mr. Hatfield, failing to see any further interest by consumers, did not want to continue the project. However, Mr. Rosato convinced him that Kennedy collectors would welcome the piece (naturally he did not want to see the medal lost to a new facet of collecting).

The first casting of the new pieces took place in early 1966—type three only. Two hundred were initially cast with the idea of possibly casting another three hundred. The medal was sold exclusively by mail order by Mr. Rosato.

The new issue actually constitutes and creates a type four, because the new issue will be sprayed with a double coat of lacquer which gives a different appearance. Collectors should beware of two facts. First, type four can be chrome-plated to appear like type one; it is therefore important to look for the copyright notice—or the absence of it. Second, though it is expected that there will be fewer type four's than type three's, it is possible that many more could be struck; if so, the difference will be in the paint color. In addition, the type four will have a smooth heavy look; the type three is coated very thinly and the metal shows through in places.

NO.	QUANTITY	SIZE	DESCRIPTION	ORIGINAL PRICE
173	100		T-1 Chrome-plated	$5.00
173-A	100		T-2 lacquered	5.00
173-B	800		T-3 lacquered	5.00
173-C	200		T-4 lacquered	2.75
173-D	1		Trial-no lettering	—

PART II

FOREIGN
MEDALS, COINS,
AND TOKENS,
BY COUNTRY

ARABIA

FIVE RUPEES OF SHARJAH

John F. Kennedy is depicted on the first dollar-sized coin of the world to bear his portrait.

Sharjah, a newly independent state on the Persian Gulf Coast of Arabia, issued its first coin, a 5 Rupee, 720 fine silver, 36mm crown-size piece dominated by a left-facing profile of Kennedy. In face value, it equals $1.05 in United States currency.

The obverse of the coin shows Kennedy's portrait, and on the left is the inscription in English: "MEMORIAL OF JOHN F. KENNEDY 1964." The same inscription is repeated in Arabic, the native language of the Trucial Coast state, on the right. Below the truncation of the bust is the designer's monogram, "R" inside a "C." The reverse is dominated by crossed Sharjah flags and the legend in English: "5 RUPEES OF SHARJAH." The legend is repeated in Arabic on the reverse. Under the left flag in tiny relief letters is "720," which indicates the fineness of the dollar-sized coin.

At the Paris, France, mint Sharjah had struck 33,000 pieces for circulation and 10,000 in proof which bear the English word "PROOF" between the flagstaffs on the reverse. The pieces are not proofs in the United States Mint standard. The coins were officially issued May 21, 1965, and the wholesaler and agent was Ant. Metcattaf et Fils, P.O. Box 1367, Beirut, Lebanon. The firm is listed as bankers, export-import wholesale coin and stamp dealers. Although most of the 43,000 coins went to dealers for sale to collectors, the sheik held 500 pieces for presentation to important people in his country.

The Sharjah Riyal ("Riyal" is Arabic and means "silver dollar") is the second coin of the world to depict Kennedy and the first such piece in dollar size. The first was the United States half dollar, dated 1964. (See No. 1.)

The proof coins are packed in a special plush box with the Kennedy portrait on it along with the inscription: "IN MEMORY OF JOHN F. KENNEDY."

Sharjah, more properly Sharjah and Dependencies, is one of seven small Arab states making up the Trucial Oman or the Trucial Coast, the area of the Persian Gulf formerly called

FIVE RUPEES OF SHARJAH

the Pirate Coast. Sharjah City itself, with about 4,000 inhabitants, is on the Persian Gulf. Its dependencies, Dhiba, Khor Fakkan, and Kalba, are on the Gulf of Oman to the south.

Since July 10, 1963, Sharjah has issued its own postage stamps based on its currency system of 100 Naye Paise equaling 1 Rupee. Five Rupees equals 1 Riyal, and the Riyal in the past has generally been the Maria Theresa Thaler, the famous Austrian coin of 1780, still in use in the area.

In theory, the Kennedy Riyal is designed to replace the Maria Theresa Riyal. The Rupee is based on that of India. This coin is termed a token by the British authorities in Dubai, residence of the British political agent for the Trucial States. The Sharjah government maintains that the specimens are coins.

The Trucial Oman extends 300 miles along the Persian Gulf between Qatar Peninsula and Cape Musandam. The British-protected area has a population of approximately 80,000, and the capital city is Sharjah.

Six Arab states, including Sharjah, entered into a treaty arrangement with Britain in 1820, following their defeat in the war with the English East India Company. By a series of agreements, especially those of 1953 and 1892, Britain undertook to suppress the slave trade and piracy and to conduct relations of the Trucial States with foreign powers.

The states are supervised by a British residency agent. Other states making up the Trucial complex include Fujeira, Ajman, Abu Dhabi, Dubai, Ras al Khaima, and Umm Al Quwain.

The ruler of Sharjah was Sheik Saqr bin Sultan al Qasimi until he was deposed on June 30, 1965, by his family because he had ordered the issue of this coin, an act which was declared an infringement on the liquidity of the Gulf Rupee. He was replaced by Sheik Khalid bin Muhammad al Qasimi.

The former ruler issued a certificate stating that the 1964-dated John F. Kennedy Memorial 5 Rupee silver coin of his country was legal tender. This affidavit, dated April 29, 1965,

94

during negotiations with the Paris, France, mint for its striking, was brought to light after the controversy.

The document was on official stationery of the ruler of Sharjah and is signed and sealed by the sheik. The certificate reads as follows: "Certificate. This is to certify that the five Rupee silver coin commemorating President John Kennedy is legal tender in Sharjah."

The question of the coin's validity is obvious; however, it may not be accepted as legal tender by the British and the present ruler of Sharjah. It is considered by the author to be a coin and legal tender based on the facts.

Sharjah has shown a tendency to cater to collector interests in the past, having issued seven commemorative stamps, including sets for space research and the Tokyo Olympics and, most recently, a set in memory of Kennedy. No coins have been issued before this Kennedy commemorative. The coins have plain edges and are distributed in the United States by Philip Berkley and Company, Ltd., 460 South Spring Street, Los Angeles, California.

Information on Sharjah, its coins, and its paper money may be obtained by writing to the General Post Office, Government of Sharjah and Dependencies.

NO.	QUANTITY	SIZE	DESCRIPTION	ORIGINAL PRICE
AR1	33,000	36mm	Silver, .720, regular issue	$5.95
AR1-A	10,000	36mm	Silver, .720, prooflike (boxed)	15.00

AUSTRIA

CHAMPION OF
FREEDOM MEDAL

The John F. Kennedy Memorial Medal was issued on the occasion of the death of the 35th President of the United States.

The medal shows on the obverse the likeness of the President with the inscription: "U.S. PRESIDENT, J. F. KENNEDY, 1917–1963."

The reverse shows the Statue of Liberty in New York City and the fifty stars of the American Star-Spangled Banner with the inscription: "DEFENSOR LIBERTARIS" (The Champion of Freedom).

This medal was designed by the famous artist Professor R. Schmidt of the Academy of Creative Artists in Vienna and has been registered with the International Bureau of Intellectual Property in Geneva.

The coinage was made at the Federal Mint in Austria, Vienna, which guarantees the gold content, the weight, and the amount of issue.

The medals were coined in limited numbers and are serially numbered on the rim. Each medal thus numbered was accompanied with a guarantee certificate bearing the identical number.

NO.	QUANTITY	SIZE	WEIGHT	DESCRIPTION	ORIGINAL PRICE
U1	1,000	50mm	50 grams	Gold, .900	$95.55
U1-A	5,000	32mm	17.5 grams	Gold, .900	35.10
U1-B	20,000	20mm	3.5 grams	Gold, .900	7.22
U1-C		50mm		Silver, .999	12.00
U1-D		40mm		Silver, .999	8.00
U1-E		30mm		Silver, .999	5.00
U1-F		21mm		Silver, .999	3.00

WELTZ MEMORIAM MEDAL

This memorial coin is the work of the academic sculptor and seal cutter Professor Weltz. His name guarantees artistic quality.

The medal was struck by the internationally famous Main Mint in Vienna. The medal was hand coined from polished dies and was struck in gold and silver.

This coin is sold by S. M. Fedridt & Co., Viena VIII, Wickenburggasse 16.

NO.	QUAN-TITY	SIZE	DESCRIPTION	WEIGHT	ORIGINAL PRICE
AU2		55mm	Gold, fine .900	100.32 grams	$439.12
AU2-A		40mm	Gold, fine .900	33.44 grams	137.50
AU2-B		33mm	Gold, fine .900	20.06 grams	80.50
AU2-C		20mm	Gold, fine .900	4.18 grams	16.75
AU2-D		12.5mm	Gold, fine .900	1.67 grams	6.75
AU2-E		7mm			
AU2-F		55mm	Proof, silver, .900, numbered edge		

KENNEDY
COMMON GOOD MEDAL

NO.	QUANTITY	SIZE	DESCRIPTION	ORIGINAL PRICE
AU3		36mm	Gold	

CANADA

CANADIAN TRIBUTE MEDAL

Wellings of Toronto, Canada, struck this medal. It is the first such medal struck in Canada honoring Kennedy. The medal, 40mm in diameter and 2mm thick at the rim, features a concave obverse field with a mirrorlike finish, while Kennedy's bust is in high relief and has a matte finish.

Elizabeth Wyn Wood designed the obverse, and her initials appear below Kennedy's bust. The reverse, designed by Roderick V. Smith, shows a wreath of maple leaves around the inscription: "IN TRIBUTE TO THE MEMORY OF PRESIDENT JOHN FITZGERALD KENNEDY/UNITED STATES OF AMERICA/HE HAD VISIONS OF NOBILITY FOR ALL MANKIND THAT TRANSCENDED MAN'S COMMON HERITAGE." A representation of the Canadian Parliament buildings and the word "CANADA" appear below the inscription. The wording on the obverse is: "JOHN FITZGERALD KENNEDY 1917–1963." A small rocking chair appears on the reverse above the inscription.

The issue was struck in 1964 and was sold through the Canada Medal and Token Company, P.O. Box 66, Aurora, Ontario, Canada, and the Canada Coin Exchange, 49 Queen Street, East Toronto 1, Canada.

NO.	QUANTITY	SIZE	DESCRIPTION	ORIGINAL PRICE
C1	20	40mm	Platinum	$600.00
C1-A	100	40mm	24k gold	175.00
C1-B	5,000	40mm	Silver, fine, .999	10.00
C1-C	Unlimited	40mm	Bronze	2.00

KENNEDY COIN MEMORIAL

The Canadian Centennial Numismatic Park at Sudbury, Ontario, the home of Canada's "Big Nickel," made a strong bid for international popularity in the spring of 1965. A medallic monument to the late President John F. Kennedy was erected there by the Nickel Monument Development, Ltd., Box 122, Sudbury, Ontario, Canada.

The Kennedy Coin Memorial is a towering 35-foot monument into which is set a detailed replica of the 1964 Kennedy Half Dollar, 20 feet in diameter, 18 inches thick, and made of nickel stainless steel. The base of the monument contains an Eternal Flame atop a pedestal of marble and nickel stainless steel.

The inscription at the base of the memorial reads: ". . . AND SO, LET THE WORD GO FORTH . . . THAT THE TORCH HAS BEEN LIT . . ." extracted from the text of the inaugural address of the assassinated President.

Since there is no fee for admission to the Canadian Centennial Numismatic Park, financing of the Kennedy Coin Memorial came strictly from the sale of the special medallic emission produced by the Welling Manufacturing Company, 67 Richmond Street, East Toronto 1, Ontario, Canada. The medallion is the first and only such piece honoring the late United States President.

The obverse of the medallion depicts a view of the erection at the unique recreation center in Sudbury, which is known as the "nickel capital of the world."

On the reverse is shown the Kennedy grave in Arlington Cemetery, Virginia, with the base inscription: "AND SO LET THE WORD GO FORTH THAT THE TORCH HAS BEEN LIT."

The medallion measures 36mm in diameter and is .105 inches thick.

The medallion was issued in platinum, gold, and silver, and is serially numbered.

106

NO.	QUANTITY	SIZE	DESCRIPTION	ORIGINAL PRICE
C2		36mm	Platinum	$500.00
C2-A		36mm	24k gold	180.00
C2-B		36mm	Silver, .999	9.00
C2-C		36mm	Nickel-silver	1.50
C2-D		36mm	Bronze-copper	1.50

ROHDE MEDAL

The obverse and reverse of this medal, which pays tribute to President John F. Kennedy, were designed by Fred and Wilma Rohde, with the portrait modeled by Andre Andrechuk. The engraving was completed by Ben Ireland. The medal was produced by Wellings Manufacturing Company and is being sold by Elizron Enterprises, Box 95, Tillsonburg, Ontario, Canada. It has a plain edge, proof, with "WELLINGS" stamped on.

NO.	QUANTITY	SIZE	DESCRIPTION	ORIGINAL PRICE
C3	1,000	51mm	Silver	$25.00
C3-A	2,000	51mm	Bronze	5.00

GOLD KENNEDY MEDALLION

This medal was struck without much fanfare as a commercial venture of the International Metals Company, 504 Victoria Avenue, Windsor, Ontario, Canada. However, it is intended as a memorial item.

The maker stated that these medals were struck and fabricated in compliance with the United States Treasury Department Gold Regulations in order to import them into the United States. However, this statement is questionable because the medals do come under the United States Gold Statute.

NO.	QUAN-TITY	SIZE	WEIGHT	DESCRIPTION	ORIGINAL PRICE
C4		32mm	1.503 ounces	24k gold	$100.00

ELIZRON MEDAL

Elizron Enterprises, P.O. Box 95, Tillsonburg, Ontario, Canada, has included this medal as one of their "World Personalities Series."

Ralph Srigley designed the medal, which was struck by Canadian Artistic Dies.

This is Elizron Enterprises' first Kennedy medal, and the firm has no plans for striking other such items.

This medal was struck with a plain edge.

NO.	QUANTITY	SIZE	DESCRIPTION	ORIGINAL PRICE
C5		20mm	24k gold, Special Order	$25.00
C5-A	500	20mm	Silver, .999	2.00
C5-B	500	20mm	Goldplated	2.00
C5-C	20,000	20mm	Bronze	.50

CHINA

KENNEDY-HONG KONG MEDAL

A novelty item similar to the many made in Japan, this piece was manufactured in Hong Kong, China, for export into the United States and was made by Kwong Sing Company of Kowloon. The obverse depicts a copy of the United States half dollar Kennedy bust. "JOHN F. KENNEDY" appears around the top and "1917/1963" around the bottom. The reverse reads "ASK/NOT WHAT YOUR/COUNTRY CAN DO/FOR YOU/ASK/WHAT YOU CAN/DO FOR YOUR/COUNTRY."

This information was received second hand and cannot be certain as the medal has not been seen by this author.

O.	QUANTITY	SIZE	DESCRIPTION	ORIGINAL PRICE
H1		30mm	Gilt	
H1-A		30mm	Gilt, looped	
H1-B		30mm	Silvered	
H1-C		30mm	Silvered, looped	

ENGLAND

CATHOLIC STATES MEDAL

The origin of this medal was a mystery during the first two years of its issue. Only a few persons knew of the medal and these thought it had been struck in the Chicago area and secretly sold by the manufacturer, an individual.

In 1965, the person who actually originated the medal sold his remaining stock and the dies to Charles McSorley, a medal dealer in Durie, New Jersey. This man had the medal struck in England by the John Pinches Company.

The medal is highly sought after.

NO.	QUANTITY	SIZE	DESCRIPTION	ORIGINAL PRICE
E1	10	32mm	Gold	
E1-A	100	32mm	Silver	$10.00
E1-B	1,000	32mm	Bronze	3.00

FRANCE

KENNEDY CANCER APPEAL

The purpose of this medal was in conjunction with an idea to form an International Kennedy Cancer Appeal Committee. The medal was to commemorate President Kennedy's death. The profit from the sale of the medal was to be devoted to cancer research. The government authorized the makers to buy gold on the free market, and the French mint agreed to strike the medal at the cost of manufacture.

After the initial planning, the maker learned that he could not import the medals into the United States since they were to be struck in gold only and the United States bans the import of gold into the country. There the project was abandoned.

The maker struck fifty pieces in bronze gilt.

The originator of the idea was Mr. A. Hurst, 11, Rue Lubeck, Paris 16E, France. The design and dies were prepared by the members of the French mint.

There is a possibility that additional medals may be struck in small quantities, but this is doubtful.

NO.	QUANTITY	SIZE	DESCRIPTION	ORIGINAL PRICE
F1	25	32mm	Bronze, gilt, plain	$7.00
F1-A	25	32mm	Bronze, gilt, looped	8.00

THE FRENCH MEDAL
CLUB MEDAL

The French Medal Club is an organization of "art lovers," which is its own description. However, the purpose and plan of this organization appear similar to the American Medal subscription programs.

The club solicits memberships which obligate members to purchase per year at least four medals issued by the club.

The club also publishes a bulletin on medallic art. Another inducement to join is a free premium medal to "loyal members."

The medals issued are numbered and struck for members only.

The French Medal Club is located at the Hotel de la Monnaie, 11, Quai du Conti; Paris VIème, France.

The first medal issued is the one shown above. The medal was designed by Albert deJaeger and was struck by the Paris mint.

NO.	QUANTITY	SIZE	DESCRIPTION	ORIGINAL PRICE
F2	400	68mm	Silvered bronze	
F2-A		68mm	Bronze	

120

GERMANY

POLITICAL LEADERS OF
THE WORLD MEDAL

Deutsche Numismatik, Frankfurt/M Untermainkai 82, Germany, issued this medal as a part of its "Political Leaders of the World Series."

The medal was struck at the State Mint in Karlsruhe, Germany.

The obverse depicts a portrait of John F. Kennedy. The inscription, "POLITICAL LEADERS IN THE WORLD," appears in both English and German, as does "U.S.A."

The reverse design consists of a flag-covered globe with the inscription reappearing in English and German.

The edge is reeded.

NO.	QUANTITY	SIZE	WEIGHT	DESCRIPTION	ORIGINAL PRICE
G1	500	50mm	70 grams	Gold, .900	$125.00
G1-A	1,000	40mm	35 grams	Gold, .900	60.00
G1-B		30mm	22.2 grams	Gold, .900	40.00
G1-C		30mm	15 grams	Gold, .900	27.50
G1-D	1,000	30mm	15 grams	Gold, rose, plain edge	
G1-E		21mm	6 grams	Gold, .900	11.25
G1-F		14mm	1.5 grams	Gold, .900	3.50
G1-G		50mm	40 grams	Silver, 1,000	7.50
G1-H		40mm	25 grams	Silver, 1,000	5.00
G1-I		30mm	13 grams	Silver, 1,000	3.50

KENNEDY ASSASSINATION MEDAL

United States

The above medal was called at the time of its issuance, "The Medal That Couldn't Be Struck." This applied to the scene of Lee Harvey Oswald's death in Dallas, which provided the original reverse die (top) for the Kennedy Assassination medal struck for Deutsche Numismatik, Untermainkai 82, Frankfurt am Main, Germany. The medal, which has a similar scene, was struck for United States release only and the motto "IN HONOREM DIEI ANNALIS CUSUS" in a wreath on the reverse for other distribution is shown below.

The piece depicted is the original trial piece, of which only three copies were struck at Karlsruhe. Deutsche Numismatik revealed: "Despite the work of our Italian artist, Professor Galdini of Italy, to prepare the reverse which also took several months, the State Mint, Karlsruhe, refused to strike it. We could only persuade them to strike three medals with original reverse and obverse." Later, Karlsruhe Mint agreed to strike the medal for the United States, only with the reverse showing the Oswald shooting. The obverse (upper right) differs in some respects from the medal below; it has the date expressed as "MCM/LXIII" while the distribution copy has "1963." The trial piece has small words, "XX DUK 986" at the bottom to indicate "20 ducats .986 fine" for use in gold. The medal was issued in November, 1964.

The trial pieces, which will eventually be one of the rarest pieces of the series, were originally acquired by the author and Jack Faulkner of Griffin, Georgia. The author received one piece and Faulkner received two pieces directly from the maker. Variety No. 1 is a newly discovered reverse.

NO.	QUANTITY	SIZE	DESCRIPTION	WEIGHT	ORIGINAL PRICE
G2	50	60mm	United States, gold, fine .986, 50 ducat	175 grams	$335.00
G2-A	150	60mm	United States, gold, fine .986, 30 ducat	105 grams	200.00

124

G2-B	300	60mm	United States, gold, fine .986, 20 ducat	70 grams	135.00
G2-C	Unlimited		United States, gold, fine .986, 5 ducat	17.5 grams	35.00
G2-D	Unlimited		United States, gold, fine .986, 2½ ducat	8.8 grams	18.75
G2-E	50	60mm	German, gold, fine .986, 50 ducat	175 grams	$335.00
G2-F	150	60mm	German, gold, fine .986, 30 ducat	105 grams	200.00
G2-G	300	60mm	German, gold, fine .986, 20 ducat	70 grams	135.00
G2-H	Unlimited		German, gold, fine .986, 5 ducat	17.5 grams	35.00
G2-I	Unlimited		German, gold, fine .986, 2½ ducat	8.5 grams	18.75
G2-J	3	30mm	Trial piece, silver, fine, 1,000	13 grams	
G2-K	10,000	60mm	United States, silver, fine, 1,000, matte	70 grams	12.50
G2-L	10,000	60mm	United States, silver, fine, 1,000, proof	70 grams	13.75
G2-M	10,000	60mm	German, silver, fine, 1,000, matte	70 grams	12.50
G2-N	10,000	60mm	German, silver, fine, 1,000, proof	70 grams	13.75

Reverse-German Issue

Variety No. 1

KENNEDY DEATH MEDAL

World-famous designer Werner Graul created this medal commemorating the death of President Kennedy.

The medal was struck by Aureus Magnus, 11, Vingerstrause, Munich, Germany.

The reverse bears the words "AUREUS MAGNUS" and is the same as medal No. G4.

NO.	QUANTITY	SIZE	DUC-AT	WEIGHT	DE-SCRIP-TION	ORIG-INAL PRICE
G3	1,000	80mm	100	350 grams	Gold, .980	$650.00
G3-A		50mm	30		Gold, .980	345.00
G3-B		50mm	20		Gold, .980	200.00
G3-C		44mm	10		Gold, .980	125.00
G3-D		35mm	5		Gold, .980	66.00
G3-E		26mm	2½		Gold, .980	40.00
G3-F		20mm	1	3.5 grams	Gold, .980	19.50
G3-G		15.5mm	½	1.8 grams	Gold, .980	11.00

126

WERNER GRAUL

Werner Graul, who was born in Berlin and considers himself a citizen of the world, has experienced two currency devaluations in his country: in 1922, after World War I, he paid 1 trillion Marks for one new "Reichsmark" that was valued at 25 cents in American money. Graul remembers how terrible the times were. After 1918, the Mark lost value daily until it was worth almost nothing. In paper money, there were bank notes for 100 and for 1 billion Marks and higher. A subway ticket cost several million Marks and became more expensive from week to week.

In 1948, after World War II, he paid 100 "Reichsmarks" for 7 "Deutsche Marks," the present currency of West Germany.

Since citizens of other countries have also suffered through currency devaluation and since, after the experiences of two world wars, the tendency toward uniting all peoples has steadily become stronger, Graul has tried to turn into reality the idea of an international currency based on gold. In 1957, he founded the Institute for International Gold Currency in Zurich, Switzerland. In *The Ten Points of Zurich* he proposed to the governments of the Western world that a uniform gold piece be coined, the "AUREUS MAGNUS," the "Great Golden One," valued at 10 ducats (1 ducat equals 3.5 grams gold, .980 fine). Even though the responses of the various governments did not produce any practical results, banks and the general public did become interested in the new gold piece. The "Great Golden One" was made under contract of banks and the Aureus Magnus Corporation in the state mints of Hamburg, Germany, and Vienna, Austria. The value of the gold pieces already issued exceeds 1 million ducats. Argenteus is the reverse of silver pieces.

ARGENTEUS DEATH MEDAL

This medal is the same as the Kennedy Death Medal, except that the reverse bears the word "ARGENTEUS" rather than the words "AUREUS MAGNUS." (See No. G3.)

NO.	SIZE	ARGENTEUS	WEIGHT	DESCRIPTION	ORIGINAL PRICE
G4	50mm	3	45 grams	Silver, 1,000	$8.00
G4-A	35mm	1	15 grams	Silver, 1,000	4.00

ARGENTEUS
DEATH MEDAL NO. 2

Werner Graul created this Kennedy medal commemorating the President's death.

The medal was struck by Aureus Magnus, 11 Vingerstrasse, Munich, Germany.

The obverse is the same as medal No.   , with the exception of the date on the field, "29/V/1917."

The reverse is the same as medal No.

Since the demand for these pieces was so great, the prices varied according to the number. The low numbers demanded a much higher price than the high numbers.

Hans Schulman of New York City was the sole distributor for the medal in the United States. He is located at 545 Fifth Avenue, New York, New York.

NO.	QUANTITY	SIZE	AR-GEN-TEUS	WEIGHT	DE-SCRIP-TION	ORIG-INAL PRICE
G5	150	80mm	100	350 grams	Gold, .980	$650.00
G5-A	2,000	80mm	10	150 grams	Silver, 1,000	48.00

129

JFK VISIT TO EUROPE— 1963 MEDAL

This coin represents a series of coins issued in honor of President Kennedy. The series is part of Germany's Aureus Magnus series. These coins are not approved for import into the United States under the United States Gold Act. However, this law does not apply to the silver varieties.

The series, struck to commemorate the historic visit of Kennedy to Germany in 1963, consists of coins of the denomination of 1 ducat, 2½ ducats, 5 ducats, 10 ducats, 20 ducats, and 30 ducats.

Although these coins carry a denomination, they are not intended for circulation.

These coins were struck at the Munich, Germany, mint. The designer is Werner Graul.

The obverse shows a left profile bust of Kennedy above a United States shield, and the legend reads: "U.S. PRESIDENT J. F. KENNEDY VISITS EUROPE 1963."

Denominations are indicated within the standard Aureus Magnus shield on the reverse of each piece. This reverse is an unchanging design for the series with an out-branching cross of lilies as a mark of world validity and it guarantees the metal content. "PRO PROSPERITATE MUNDI" (For the World's Prosperity) is inscribed at the top; at the bottom is "AUREUS MAGNUS." In the center of the cross is the denomination in ducats.

The pieces were struck in late 1963 and early 1964.

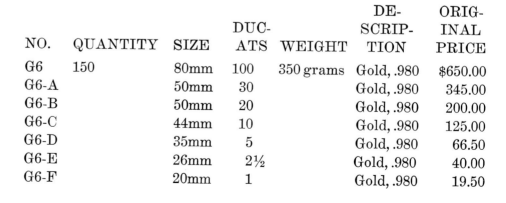

NO.	QUANTITY	SIZE	DUC-ATS	WEIGHT	DE-SCRIP-TION	ORIG-INAL PRICE
G6	150	80mm	100	350 grams	Gold, .980	$650.00
G6-A		50mm	30		Gold, .980	345.00
G6-B		50mm	20		Gold, .980	200.00
G6-C		44mm	10		Gold, .980	125.00
G6-D		35mm	5		Gold, .980	66.50
G6-E		26mm	2½		Gold, .980	40.00
G6-F		20mm	1		Gold, .980	19.50

ARGENTEUS VISIT MEDAL

This medal is the same as the JFK VISIT TO EUROPE-1963 MEDAL, described previously, except that the reverse changes with the words "Aureus Magnus" being replaced by the word "ARGENTEUS." (See No. G4.)

NO.	SIZE	ARGENTEUS	WEIGHT	DESCRIPTION	ORIG-INAL PRICE
G7	50mm	3	45 grams	Silver, 1,000	$8.00
G7-A	35mm	1	15 grams	Silver, 1,000	4.00

KENNEDY-LIBERTY MEDAL

This medal became known to the author at the last moment before publication, and thus research was not possible. However, it is known that the medal was struck in 1960 for President Kennedy's election to the Presidency.

The medal is a German piece and most likely was struck in Germany.

Sales of the piece were made through banks and savings institutions in Germany.

The fifty stars symbolize the fifty states and the unity of the United States. The gold content is guaranteed.

NO.	QUAN-TITY	SIZE	DESCRIPTION	WEIGHT	ORIG-INAL PRICE
G8		49mm	Gold, pure ducat, .980, fine, 20 ducat	70 grams	$125.00
G8-A		39mm	Gold, pure ducat, .980, fine, 10 ducat	35 grams	62.50
G8-B		30mm	Gold, pure ducat, .980, fine, 5 ducat	17.5 grams	31.25
G8-C		25mm	Gold, pure ducat, .980, fine, 3 ducat	10.5 grams	18.75
G8-D		20mm	Gold, pure ducat, .980, fine, 1 ducat	3.5 grams	7.50

SHRIVER-KENNEDY PEACE CORPS MEDAL

In 1961, an old idea became a reality, thanks to the initiative of John F. Kennedy and his brother-in-law Sargent Shriver, then the President of the Department of Education in Chicago. The idea of the Peace Corps grew surprisingly fast into a program that functioned efficiently on a transoceanic, worldwide basis.

John F. Kennedy created the basis, uniting authority and power, assuring the material conditions to oppose criticism and to overcome skepticism and fear.

Studies of many years and the experiences from universities, institutes, and missionary groups eventually formed the basis for Executive Order No. 10924 of March 1, 1961, which introduced the charter document of the Peace Corps. Through the Peace Corps Act of Congress of September, 1961, the young organization has been empowered to serve world peace and foster the friendship of all interested countries through voluntary helpers from all professions, including scientists, teachers, doctors, and technicians who serve in these countries in order to fill the lack of skilled manpower, produce better understanding of America, erase need, energetically solve human problems, and improve, as much as is possible, the social standard.

This gigantic task justifies the extremely exacting aptitude tests of character and knowledge to which each candidate for the Corps is subjected.

This medal was struck at the Bavarian Head Mint in Munich, Germany, in tribute to the worldwide, peace-serving program, the acute political importance of which should not be underestimated in view of the competing efforts of the Communist nations.

The medals were coined in limited quantities and are consecutively numbered on the edge and carry a guarantee seal.

The medal was designed by Heino P. Meissl.

NO.	QUAN-TITY	SIZE	DESCRIPTION	WEIGHT	ORIG-INAL PRICE
G9	150	50mm	Gold, fine .900	175 grams	
G9-A	200	50mm	Gold, fine .900	140 grams	
G9-B	500	50mm	Gold, fine .900	105 grams	
G9-C	500	50mm	Gold, fine .900	70 grams	
G9-D	Unlimited	40mm	Gold, fine .900	35 grams	
G9-E	Unlimited	32mm	Gold, fine .900	17.5 grams	
G9-F	Unlimited	26mm	Gold, fine .900	10.5 grams	
G9-G	Unlimited	20mm	Gold, fine .900	3.5 grams	
G9-H	Unlimited	40mm	Silver, fine 1,000	25 grams	

KENNEDY-ADENAUER
MEDAL NO. 2

This medal was struck by Hoffstatter Company of Bonn, Germany, and was designed by Ingebord von Rath. It is one of the most beautiful and unusual of medals. The design and workmanship differs from anything known to the author. The busts on the obverse are inset (relief in reverse).

The designer's initials, below Kennedy's chin, are "VR." At the bottom, on the reverse, in small letters, are the words "HOFFSTATTER BONN 1000" for metal fineness.

NO.	QUANTITY	SIZE	DESCRIPTION	ORIGINAL PRICE
G10		50mm	Gold	
G10-A		50mm	Silver	
G10-B		50mm	Bronze	

KENNEDY WELCOME
IN GERMANY MEDAL

Designed in 1963 by Albert Holl, this medal was struck by
Staatliche Munze of Karlsruhe, Germany.

NO.	QUANTITY	SIZE	WEIGHT	DESCRIPTION	ORIG-INAL PRICE
G11		50mm	70 grams	Gold, .900	$120.00
G11-A		40mm	40 grams	Gold, .900	70.00
G11-B		25mm	14 grams	Gold, .900	24.00
G11-C		50mm	46 grams	Silver, 1,000	7.00
G11-D		40mm	25 grams	Silver, 1,000	5.00

HOLL-WHITE HOUSE MEDAL

This medal was designed by Albert Holl and was struck by Staatliche Munze of Karlsruhe, Germany.

NO.	QUANTITY	SIZE	WEIGHT	DESCRIPTION	ORIG- INAL PRICE
G12	500	65mm	150 grams	Gold, .986	$277.00
G12-A		50mm	70 grams	Gold, .900	120.00
G12-B		40mm	40 grams	Gold, .900	70.00
G12-C		25mm	14 grams	Gold, .900	24.00
G12-D		22.5mm	8 grams	Gold, .900	13.00
G12-E		65mm	90 grams	Silver, 1,000, matte	15.00
G12-F	1,000	65mm	90 grams	Silver, 1,000, proof	18.00
G12-G		50mm	45 grams	Silver, 1,000, matte	7.50
G12-H		40mm	25 grams	Silver, 1,000, matte	5.00
G12-I		40mm	25 grams	Silver, 1,000, proof	6.00

HOLL MEMORIAM MEDAL

This medal was designed by Albert Holl and was struck by Staatliche Munze of Karlsruhe, Germany.

NO.	QUANTITY	SIZE	WEIGHT	DESCRIPTION	ORIGINAL PRICE
G13	125	85mm	350 grams	Gold, .986	$637.00
G13-A	250	75mm	250 grams	Gold, .986	456.00
G13-B	500	65mm	150 grams	Gold, .986	277.00
G13-C		50mm	70 grams	Gold, .900	120.00
G13-D		40mm	40 grams	Gold, .900	70.00
G13-E		25mm	14 grams	Gold, .900	24.00
G13-F		22.5mm	8 grams	Gold, .900	13.00
G13-G		85mm	180 grams	Silver, 1,000, matte	30.00
G13-H	250	85mm	180 grams	Silver, 1,000, proof	37.00
G13-I		75mm	130 grams	Silver, 1,000, matte	22.00
G13-J	500	75mm	130 grams	Silver, 1,000, proof	27.00
G13-K		65mm	90 grams	Silver, 1,000, matte	15.00
G13-L	1,000	65mm	90 grams	Silver, 1,000, proof	18.00
G13-M		50mm	45 grams	Silver, 1,000, matte	7.50
G13-N		40mm	25 grams	Silver, 1,000, matte	5.00
G13-O		40mm	25 grams	Silver, 1,000, proof	6.00

137

NUMMIS MUNDI MEDAL
"COINS OF THE WORLD"

Nummis Mundi, Latin for "Coins of the World," is an identification mark of this series.

The reverse is an historic coat of arms from the early ages, the symbol of this international series which includes John F. Kennedy.

NO.	QUAN-TITY	SIZE	WEIGHT	DESCRIPTION	ORIG-INAL PRICE
G14		50mm	100 grams	Gold, .999	$212.50
G14-A		34mm	30 grams	Gold, .999	62.50
G14-B		34mm	16 grams	Gold, .999	32.50
G14-C		26mm	8 grams	Gold, .999	17.50
G14-D		20mm	3.5 grams	Gold, .999	12.50
G14-E		50mm	50 grams	Silver, 1,000	9.50
G14-F		34mm	15 grams	Silver, 1,000	3.50

KENNEDY-ADENAUER,
MUNICH MEDAL

In honor of John F. Kennedy's birthday, May 29, the Bavarian Mint reissued the three silver medals it struck to commemorate his career as the 35th President of the United States.

The medal was struck for the occasion of President Kennedy's visit to Germany on June 26, 1963.

It was struck by the Bavarian State Mint at Munich and was designed by Professor F. Breitholz.

The same reverse is used for the Kennedy-Peace Dove Medal (see No. G17), which was also issued by the Bavarian State Mint.

The International Coin and Medal Company, 550 Fifth Avenue, New York City, was the selling agent for the United States. The series, which consisted of three medals, The Kennedy–Peace Dove Medal, The President Kennedy "Memorial" Medal, and the Kennedy-Adenauer, Munich Medal, were sold together, boxed, and were also struck in gold.

O.	QUANTITY	SIZE	WEIGHT	DESCRIP-TION	ORIG-INAL PRICE
15	1,000	50mm	175 grams	Gold, .900	$310.00
15-A	2,000	50mm	140 grams	Gold, .900	250.00
15-B	2,500	50mm	105 grams	Gold, .900	180.00
15-C	3,000	50mm	70 grams	Gold, .900	125.00
15-D		40mm	35 grams	Gold, .900	65.00
15-E		32mm	17.5 grams	Gold, .900	31.00
15-F		26mm	10.5 grams	Gold, .900	20.00
15-G		20mm	3.5 grams	Gold, .900	6.00
15-H	1,000	40mm	25 grams	Silver, 1,000	50.00

PRESIDENT KENNEDY "MEMORIAL"

In honor of the late President Kennedy's birth date, May 29, the Bavarian State Mint at Munich reissued this medal as a commemorative. It is the memorial medal issued after the President's assassination on November 22, 1963.

The obverse is the same as the Kennedy–Peace Dove Medal (see No. G17) but does not bear the inaugural date.

The reverse bears the inscription in German, "WIR ALLE HABEN IHN VERLOREN," which means "WE HAVE ALL LOST HIM." Under the date, "22.NOV.1963," is a reposing cross. A single branch lies across the foot of the cross.

The German company which sold the medal was Merkur-Bank of Horowicz. The medals were issued in limited quantities and are numbered on the edge. "BAVARIAN STATE MINT, MUNICH" is stamped on the edge as a guarantee of content of metal fineness.

The medal was designed by Mueller and Professor F. Breitholz.

NO.	QUANTITY	SIZE	WEIGHT	DESCRIPTION	ORIGINAL PRICE
G16	1,000	60mm	175 grams	Gold, .900	$310.00
G16-A	1,500	60mm	140 grams	Gold, .900	250.00
G16-B	2,000	50mm	105 grams	Gold, .900	180.00
G16-C	2,500	50mm	70 grams	Gold, .900	125.00
G16-D		40mm	35 grams	Gold, .900	62.00
G16-E		32mm	17.5 grams	Gold, .900	31.00
G16-F		26mm	10.5 grams	Gold, .900	18.00
G16-G		20mm	3.5 grams	Gold, .900	6.00
G16-H	1,000	60mm		Silver, 1,000	
G16-I	1,000	50mm		Silver, 1,000	
G16-J	1,000	40mm		Silver, 1,000	

KENNEDY-PEACE DOVE
MEDAL

In honor of President Kennedy, the Bavarian State Mint at Munich, Germany, struck this medal.

The medal was originally struck and issued for President Kennedy's Inauguration on January 20, 1961. After Kennedy's death, the medal was reissued. (See No. G16.)

The medal was designed by Professor F. Breitholz, a noted designer in Germany.

The reverse is the same as the Kennedy-Adenauer Medal No. 1 (see No. G15).

NO.	QUAN-TITY	SIZE	WEIGHT	DESCRIPTION	ORIG-INAL PRICE
G17		40mm	35 grams	Gold, .900	$62.00
G17-A		32mm	17.5 grams	Gold, .900	31.00
G17-B		25mm	10.5 grams	Gold, .900	18.00
G17-C		20mm	3.49 grams	Gold, .900	6.00
G17-D		40mm		Silver, 1,000	5.00

141

JFK–TORCH AND BELL MEDAL

This medal was designed by Professor F. Brietholz. It was struck at the Bavarian State Mint in Munich, Germany, and was sold by Merkur-Bank.

The obverse is the same as the President Kennedy Memorial Medal (see No. G16).

NO.	QUANTITY	SIZE	WEIGHT	DESCRIP-TION	ORIG-INAL PRICE
G18	200	60mm	175 grams	Gold, .900	$310.00
G18-A	300	60mm	140 grams	Gold, .900	250.00
G18-B	500	50mm	105 grams	Gold, .900	180.00
G18-C	1,500	50mm	70 grams	Gold, .900	125.00
G18-D		40mm	35 grams	Gold, .900	62.00
G18-E		32mm	17.5 grams	Gold, .900	31.00
G18-F		26mm	10.5 grams	Gold, .900	18.00
G18-G		20mm	3.5 grams	Gold, .900	6.00
G18-H		40mm	25 grams	Silver, 1,000	5.00

STEINBERG-KENNEDY INAUGURATION MEDAL

This medal was struck by Feig and Company, a private medalist in Frankfurt/Main, Germany, for William Fox Steinberg, an American numismatist and rare coin dealer. Steinberg sold the United States distribution rights to the Welles Company of Kansas City, Missouri.

The medal was originally struck in 1960, after Kennedy's election. After the assassination, the medal was reissued and became popular.

The original sales price of $5 for the .925 sterling silver medal was increased to $10 when it was reissued.

The quantity struck was advertised by the Welles Company as 8,500 numbered pieces; however, this was an error. The exact number struck is said to be 5,500, but because of facts known to the author it is possible that upward of 15,000 were struck, half of which were distributed in Europe. The history of the medal is questionable.

The medal was also struck in gold, .980 fine. The total mintage of these is also unavailable, although it is sure that they were very limited and scarce. The price was never established for the gold piece.

It might be noted that many foreign issues were misrepresented as to price and mintage. Usually, the medalists were interested only to the extent of commercial gain. Cases have been known in which only a thousand of an issue were to be struck, but because of the popularity of the medal the amount struck exceeded the original number.

The reissue of this piece found some dealers goldplating the silver pieces. These can be distinguished by noting the gold content inscribed on the real gold pieces and not on the plated specimens.

NO.	QUANTITY	SIZE	DESCRIPTION	ORIGINAL PRICE
G19		37mm	Gold, .980	
G19-A		37mm	Goldplated	
G19-B		37mm	Silver, .925	$5.00

FEIG MEMORIAL MEDAL

Feig and Company, Medaillen K. G. of Frankfurt/Main, West Germany, struck this medal.

The medal has one obverse and is issued with three different reverses. It is a companion piece to the Jacqueline Kennedy Medal (see No. G22).

The medal was originally sold at the 1964–65 New York World's Fair by the United States Coin Corporation.

The following information applies to each piece with a different reverse, as numbered.

NO.	QUANTITY	SIZE	WEIGHT	DESCRIPTION	ORIGINAL PRICE
G20	5,000	36mm	16 grams	No. 1 gold	$26.00
G20-A	5,000	26mm	8 grams	No. 1. gold	13.00
G20-B	5,000	20mm	3.5 grams	No. 1. gold	6.00
G20-C	Unlimited	36mm		No. 1. silver	5.00
G20-D	Unlimited	26mm		No. 1. silver	4.00
G20-E	Unlimited	20mm		No. 1. silver	3.00
G20-F	5,000	36mm	16 grams	No. 2. gold	26.00
G20-G	5,000	26mm	8 grams	No. 2. gold	13.00
G20-H	5,000	20mm	3.5 grams	No. 2. gold	6.00
G20-I		36mm		No. 2. silver	5.00
G20-J		26mm		No. 2. silver	4.00
G20-K		20mm		No. 2. silver	3.00
G20-L	5,000	36mm	16 grams	No. 3. gold	26.00
G20-M	5,000	26mm	8 grams	No. 3. gold	13.00
G20-N	5,000	20mm	3.5 grams	No. 3. gold	6.00
G20-O		36mm		No. 3. silver	5.00
G20-P		26mm		No. 3. silver	4.00
G20-Q		20mm		No. 3. silver	3.00

XX

1   2   3

FEIG MEMORIAL MEDAL NO. 2

This medal was struck by Feig and Company.

The obverse bears the same Kennedy bust as the Feig Memorial Medal, No. G20. However, the inscription is different.

The reverse is the same as the Steinberg-Kennedy Inauguration Medal, No. G19.

NO.	QUANTITY	SIZE	DESCRIPTION	ORIGINAL PRICE
G21		37mm	Gold, .980	
G21-A		37mm	Silver, .925	

JACQUELINE KENNEDY MEDAL

Issued in honor of Jacqueline Kennedy, wife of assassinated President John F. Kennedy. Destined by her husband as First Lady of the United States, she met her tasks and obligations with such charm and conscience that she enjoyed love and popularity throughout the world. She is an exemplary personality and mother.

Feig and Company of Frankfurt/Main, Germany, struck and issued this medal.

NO.	QUANTITY	SIZE	WEIGHT	DESCRIPTION	ORIGINAL PRICE
G22	5,000	36mm	16 grams	Gold	$26.00
G22-A	5,000	26mm	8 grams	Gold	13.00
G22-B	5,000	20mm	3.5 grams	Gold	6.00
G22-C		36mm		Silver	5.00
G22-D		26mm		Silver	4.00
G22-E		20mm		Silver	3.00

BERLIN WALL MEDAL

Designed by Professor Hanisch Consee of Austria. "Han-Con" appears under the neck. This mark of the designer also appears on the reverse in the form of "HA-CON." It has a plain edge. There is .925 sterling on the edge of the silver pieces.

NO.	QUANTITY	SIZE	DESCRIPTION	ORIGINAL PRICE
G23		40mm	Sterling silver	
G23-A		40mm	Bronze	

DRAPED CROSS MEDAL

Designed by Professor Hanisch Consee, the bust of Kennedy is identical to the bust on No. G23, described previously. "HAN CON" appears below the neck and around the star on the reverse.

NO.	QUANTITY	SIZE	DESCRIPTION	ORIGINAL PRICE
G24		40mm	Bronze	

PREISSLER MEDAL

This piece was struck and issued by Josef Preissler of Pforzheim, Germany.

The medal is looped with a plain edge.

NO.	QUANTITY	SIZE	DESCRIPTION	ORIGINAL PRICE
G25		32mm	Goldplated	
G25-A		24mm	Goldplated	
G25-B		20mm	Goldplated	
G25-C		17mm	Goldplated	
G25-D		12mm	Goldplated	

MEN AND IDEAS MEDAL

This medal is referred to and considered by many to be a German piece. However, it was struck in Milan, Italy, by Sirom.

Professor Constantino Affer designed it.

On the reverse, under the chain, is the manufacturer's mark and ".900" for gold fineness. The edge is plain.

NO.	QUANTITY	SIZE	DESCRIPTION	ORIGINAL PRICE
G26		40mm	Gold, .900	
G26-A		32mm	Gold, .900	
G26-B		26mm	Gold, .900	
G26-C		25mm	Gold, .900	
G26-D		20mm	Gold, .900	

147

GREAT CATHOLIC MEN MEDAL

This piece was struck in Germany. One of the cleaner, more beautiful designs, the medal is raised and bears a plain edge and looped rim.

NO.	QUANTITY	SIZE	DESCRIPTION	ORIGINAL PRICE
G27		32mm	Gold, anodized aluminum	
G27-A			Silver, anodized aluminum	

THREE GREAT PRESIDENTS MEDAL

This medal was issued by Merkur-Bank of Germany.

NO.	QUANTITY	SIZE	WEIGHT	DESCRIPTION	ORIGINAL PRICE
G28	500	40mm	70 grams	Gold, .900	$162.00
G28-A		28mm	21 grams	Gold, .900	50.00
G28-B		40mm	40 grams	Silver, 1,000	10.00
G28-C		28mm	15 grams	Silver, 1,000	5.00

ARGOR MEMORIAL MEDAL

It has a reeded edge.

NO.	QUANTITY	SIZE	DESCRIPTION	ORIGINAL PRICE
G29		34mm	Gold, .900	

KENNEDY GOLD STAMP

This is the second such known piece for which a replica of a postage stamp was made in gold.

The medal was designed by Hans Ketterer of Hanau, near Frankfurt, Germany, and was struck, with a plain edge, by Fa. Haeraeus, Edelmetalle of Hanau.

NO.	QUANTITY	SIZE	DESCRIPTION	ORIGINAL PRICE
G30		21 × 24mm	Gold, .986	

PHILATELIC IN GOLD

Munzen Und Medaillen Motek Horowicz and Company of Munich, Germany, has issued this replica of a United States stamp in gold.

NO.	QUANTITY	SIZE	DESCRIPTION	ORIGINAL PRICE
G31	20,000	39 × 24mm	Gold	$52.25

149

HOLLAND

CIVIL RIGHTS ACT MEDAL

This medal was struck for Martin Luther King in the interest of Civil Rights.

President Kennedy undertook the sponsorship for the Negro minister and, thereby, King was honored for his struggle in the Civil Rights Movement.

N. V. Koninklijke Begeer created this medal in high relief. It was designed by Willem Vis and struck in matte and proof mint gold.

A total of 2,000 medals was struck, after which the dies were destroyed.

The medals were struck for and sold by N. V. Koninklijke Begeer of Voorschoten, Holland.

NO.	QUAN-TITY	SIZE	WEIGHT	DESCRIPTION	ORIG-INAL PRICE
H1	2,000	38mm	50 grams	Matte, gold, .900	$90.25
H1-A	2,000	38mm	50 grams	Proof, gold, .900	90.25
H1-B		25mm	8.2 grams	Matte, gold, .900	16.00
H1-C		25mm	8.2 grams	Proof, gold, .900	16.00
H1-D		18.5mm	4.2 grams	Matte, gold, .900	9.75
H1-E		70mm	135 grams	Sterling silver	16.65
H1-F		38mm	27 grams	Sterling silver	4.70
H1-G		25mm	7.5 grams	Sterling silver	2.10
H1-H		70mm		Bronze	18.05
H1-I		38mm		Bronze	1.35

DUTCH PEACE CORPS
MEMORIAL MEDAL

This medal, issued and struck by N. V. Koninklijke Begeer in Voorschoten, Holland, was designed by Pol Dom and was struck in gold, silver, and bronze.

The profit from the sale of this medal was donated to the special fund of the Dutch Peace Corps, an upshot of the United States foundation sponsored by President Kennedy.

Wholesalers, banks, and coin dealers distributed the medal without profit in the interest of this work.

The Royal Mint issued these pieces, each numbered by special public authorization.

NO.	QUAN-TITY	SIZE	WEIGHT	DESCRIPTION	ORIG-INAL PRICE
H2	2,000	25mm	8.5 grams	Gold, .900	$17.25
H2-A	2,000	18.5mm	4.5 grams	Gold, .900	6.95
H2-B		70mm	140 grams	Sterling silver	18.05
H2-C		40mm	30 grams	Sterling silver	5.00
H2-D		25mm	7.5 grams	Sterling silver	1.75
H2-E		70mm		Bronze	2.70
H2-F		40mm		Bronze	1.25

ITALY

FOSSA MEMORIAM MEDAL

This medal was designed by Franco Fossa and was struck by Numismatica Italiana of Milan, Italy.

Individually numbered on the edge, each medal is accompanied by a numbered certificate. A total of 3,000 "C" medals was struck. Numbers 1 to 300 of all the medals were reserved for complete sets.

This medal was originally sold by Johnson Matthey and Company, Ltd., London, England.

NO.	QUAN-TITY	SIZE	WEIGHT	DESCRIPTION	ORIG-INAL PRICE
I3	3,000	40mm	1.125 ounces	18k gold	$81.00
I3-A		30mm	.652 ounces	18k gold	39.00
I3-B		20mm	.257 ounces	18k gold	20.00

KHRUSHCHEV-KENNEDY MEDAL

This medal was struck by Euronummus, Milan, Italy, to commemorate the meeting of President Kennedy and Soviet Premier Khrushchev in Vienna in 1961.

The medal was designed by Constantino Affer.

NO.	QUANTITY	SIZE	DESCRIPTION	ORIGINAL PRICE
I4		33mm	Gold	
I4-A		33mm	Silver	

AFFER LIBERTY MEDAL

This medal was designed by Constantino Affer and struck in Milan, Italy, by Euronummus.

NO.	QUANTITY	SIZE	DESCRIPTION	ORIGINAL PRICE
I5		60mm	Gold	
I5-A		50mm	Gold	
I5-B		40mm	Gold	
I5-C		40mm	Silver	

PIRRONE-KENNEDY MEDAL

Guiseppe Pirrone designed this medal, which was struck in Italy.

NO.	QUANTITY	SIZE	DESCRIPTION	ORIGINAL PRICE
I6		95mm	Cast	

157

INAUGURATION SPEECH MEDAL

This medal was struck in Italy.

NO.	QUANTITY	SIZE	DESCRIPTION	ORIGINAL PRICE
I7		50mm	Silver	$4.50

MEMORIAL MEDAL OF JOHN F. KENNEDY

Avrea Numismatica (Golden Numismatics), artistic coinage and precious medals, D1 Valerio Farina, Via Cesare Battisti 34, Modena, Italy, struck and issued this beautiful medal known as the "Memorial Medal of John F. Kennedy, President of the U.S.A. 1961/1963."

The sculptor was Emilio Monte.

Official word from the medalists states certain facts which have been proven incorrect by the discovery of additional items. They state that the silver and bronze were struck in only 45mm size. Listed is a 60mm size. Also, they claim only gold, silver, and bronze; however, listed is a cast piece in an

Variation 1

unidentified metal, possibly iron, or it could be an unfinished silver piece. The author has seen a 60mm gold piece which was described as unique.

The 60 and 45mm gold pieces have the words "S. JOHNSON—ITALY" in raised letters at the lower left side on the rim. This also appears on the silver pieces but not on the bronze or smaller gold pieces. I assume that Johnson is the name of the company that struck the pieces.

The engraver's name, "E. MONTE," appears on the larger gold pieces to the left of Kennedy's neck in raised letters. It also appears this way on the bronze pieces. However, in the silver pieces, the name is indented. The 20mm gold piece has only the initials in the same position; it also carries an indistinguishable stamp mark after the "t" in "PRESIDENT," and ".900" is stamped on the rim just before the "J" in "JOHN" on the obverse.

Variation 2

NO.	QUANTITY	SIZE	WEIGHT	DESCRIPTION	ORIGINAL PRICE
I8		60mm		Gold, .900	
I8-A	1,000	45mm	60 grams	Gold, .900	$200.00
I8-B		30mm	20 grams	Gold, .900	72.00
I8-C		20mm	8 grams	Gold, .900	29.00
I8-D		20mm	5 grams	Gold, .900	
I8-E		60mm		Silver, 1,000	30.00
I8-F		45mm		Silver, 1,000	15.00
I8-G		45mm		Bronze	5.00
I8-H		60mm		Obverse with "JANUARY 1961," cast silver	10.00

Variation 3

Variation 4

KENNEDY PRESIDENTIAL SEAL MEDAL

This medal, as the Kennedy Commemorative Medal, is a mystery. The only information available is from a Canadian dealer who has them struck in Italy by order from A. E. Lorioli of Milan.

The designer of this medal is Professor Constantino Affer.

The whole matter surrounding these medals is that they are struck without regard for mintage; they are a purely commercial item. They have a plain edge.

The dealer offers the same medal in fine silver and gold but only on order. Advertisements list it as silver; however, this is questionable because the price is inconsistent. It is suspected that the silver pieces are only plated.

NO.	QUANTITY	SIZE	DESCRIPTION	ORIGINAL PRICE
I9		100mm	Silver	$20.00
I9-A		50mm	Goldplated	5.75
I9-B		50mm	Silver	4.50
I9-C		33mm	Silverplated, looped	1.50
I9-D		32mm	Silver	2.50
I9-E		32mm	Goldplated	2.50
I9-F		28mm	Silver, looped	1.50
I9-G		25mm	Silver, looped	1.50

ITALIAN KENNEDY ASSASSINATION MEDAL

This piece is an exact copy of the original Deutsche Numismatik medal No. G2.

The medal was struck in Italy and was issued by Numismatica Franco-Tedisco, Largo Messico, 6, Rome, Italy.

It was issued in a special case with a certificate of guarantee.

The medal has a reeded edge.

NO.	QUANTITY	SIZE	DESCRIPTION	ORIGINAL PRICE
I10		30mm	Silver, .925, matte, proof	

COCEPA MEDAL

This medal was struck with a plain edge by Cocepa of Milan, Italy. It has no legend.

NO.	QUANTITY	SIZE	DESCRIPTION	ORIGINAL PRICE
I11	2,000	43mm	Gold	
I11-A	5,000	32mm	Gold	
I11-B	7,000	26mm	Gold	
I11-C	10,000	21mm	Gold	
I11-D		43mm	Silver	

INAUGURATION
COMMEMORATIVE MEDAL

The Italian Commemorative Medal depicted above has resulted in the biggest Kennedy mystery of all issues. The original was issued in a 50mm size and was sold exclusively through the Regency Coin and Stamp Company, 157 Rupert Street, Winnipeg, Manitoba, Canada. The medal was advertised as 50mm silver for $3.25, but closer examination reveals that the medal is not silver but is rather silverplated brass. It has also been discovered that, although the same bust was used, many die varieties have appeared. The main difference is the sculptor. One variety is signed by Affer. Also found is a light bronze variety of the same size—this is the scarce item.

The maker or medalist has been identified after exhaustive research: A. E. Lorioli Fratelli of Milan, Italy.

Another unusual aspect of this design is that the basic design and bust have been used for several other medals of smaller size, issued by American companies. One of these was issued by Swank Men's Jewelers as a key ring selling for $2.50, both in silverplate and gold-colored bronze. A second one is a plain 33mm size piece with the "ASK NOT" inscription on the reverse.

More recent to the publication of this work, a Canadian dealer began selling this medal in silverplate and goldplate.

It is expected that some time will pass before all of the varieties are discovered, since it appears that many people are using this particular design for commercial purposes without regard for the original copyright or the designer's rights. At the present time, we have found six varieties. One of these, it must be noted, is not a true medal but rather a shell using only the obverse; it is used as a piece for plaques and desk paper weights. The edge is plain.

162

NO.	QUAN-TITY	SIZE	DESCRIPTION	ORIGINAL PRICE
I12		21mm	Gold .750	
I12-A		50mm	Goldplated, Italy, horizontal to rim	$4.75
I12-B		50mm	Silverplated, Affer, Italy	4.75
I12-C		50mm	Silverplated shell, Affer, Italy	3.50
I12-D		33mm	Silverplated, Affer, Italy, "Ask Not" reverse	2.00
I12-E		33mm	Silverplated, looped, Affer, Italy, "Ask Not" reverse	2.50
I12-F		50mm	Bronze, Affer, Italy	3.50
I12-G		33mm	Bronzed, gilt, without Affer, Italy, looped, "Ask Not" reverse	2.50
I12-H		40 × 26mm	Gilt, Affer-Italy key ring medal. Flag in color	1.50

FOSSA-KENNEDY MEDAL

Designed by Franco Fossa, this medal was struck by Numismatica Italiana of Milan, Italy.

NO.	QUANTITY	SIZE	DESCRIPTION	ORIGINAL PRICE
I13		180mm	Cast bronze	
I13-A		40mm	Gold	

KENNEDY-POPE PAUL PEACE MEDAL

Professor Constantino Affer designed this piece. It was struck by Sirom K. G. of Milan, Italy.

The obverse depicts a large bust of Kennedy facing left. "JOHN F. KENNEDY" appears around the left rim and "U.S. PRESIDENT" around the right rim with "1917, 1963" to the left and right of the neck. The reverse shows a half figure of the Statue of Liberty. Around the outside is "MANKIND MUST PUT AN END TO WAR/—OR WAR WILL PUT AN END TO MANKIND." On the field is "JOHN F. KENNEDY/25-9-1961/H.H. POPE PAULUS VI/4-10-1965."

NO.	QUANTITY	SIZE	DESCRIPTION	ORIGINAL PRICE
I14		40mm	Gold	
I14-A		32mm	Gold	
I14-B		28mm	Gold	
I14-C		24mm	Gold	
I14-D		20mm	Gold	

MILAN SPORT
CENTER MEDAL

This medal was designed by Professor Constantino Affer and struck by A. E. Lorioli Fratelli of Milan, Italy. The medal commemorates the President Kennedy Sports Center dedicated August 29, 1964, in Milan. The obverse depicts an unusual bust of Kennedy extending from the top to the base of the medal. "COST. AFFER" appears at the neck. The reverse has a shield with a cross, capped with a crown. The legend reads: "INAUGURAZIONE/CENTRO SPORTIVO/ "PRESIDENTE KENNEDY"/MILANO/29 AGOSTO 1964." It has a plain edge.

NO.	QUANTITY	SIZE	DESCRIPTION	ORIGINAL PRICE
I15		42mm	Silver	

JAPAN

"IN MEMORY OF" CHARM

The obverse is the American flag in red, white, and blue, with fifty stars. The reverse has a left-facing bust of Kennedy. "IN MEMORY" is above the head. "JOHN F. KENNEDY/1917–1963" is below. It has an enameled obverse and a plain edge, looped.

It is manufactured in Japan as a novelty item.

NO.	QUANTITY	SIZE	DESCRIPTION	ORIGINAL PRICE
J1		20 × 22mm	Silvered	$1.00

JAPAN MEMORIAL MEDAL

This medal, as others shown in this section, was made in Japan by novelty manufacturers for export. It is crudely made, as are most items of this nature made in that country.

The obverse has a left-facing bust of Kennedy with "1917" to the left of the head and "1963" to the right. "JOHN F. KENNEDY" appears above the head and "35th PRESIDENT-U.S.A." around the bottom. The reverse is plain with a beaded border. It has a plain edge.

NO.	QUANTITY	SIZE	DESCRIPTION	ORIGINAL PRICE
J2		38mm	Zinc	

168

KENNEDY LIGHTER

This is another of the many novelty items produced in Japan and exported to the United States. It has a plain edge, looped. A lighter pulls out from the side.

NO.	QUANTITY	SIZE	DESCRIPTION	ORIGINAL PRICE
J3		36mm, 8mm thick	Gilt, prooflike surface	$1.00
J3-A		36mm, 8mm thick	Silvered, prooflike surface	1.00

169

KENNEDY-WHITE HOUSE LIGHTER

Manufactured in Japan for export into the United States, this item is scarce. It is a desk or table ornament, in the style and design of a medal. The side pulls out to become a Zippo-type lighter.

The obverse depicts a Gilroy Roberts bust of Kennedy taken from the United States Kennedy Half Dollar. "JOHN F. KENNEDY" appears around the top above the head; "35th PRESIDENT OF UNITED STATES" is around the bottom. The two inscriptions are separated on each side by two stars. The dates "1961" and "1963" are left and right of the neck line. The field has a beaded surface with a higher relief beaded border. The bust and letters are prooflike.

The reverse depicts the White House with the words "WHITE HOUSE" above and "LIBERTY" below. The upper half of the field consists of horizontal lines. The lower half is a beaded surface with a high relief beaded border. The White House is prooflike surface. A small eagle is attached at the top as a handle for the lighter section pull-out. It has a plain edge, prooflike.

It is sold with black metal base, 198mm × 100mm, 20mm thick.

NO.	QUANTITY	SIZE	DESCRIPTION	ORIGINAL PRICE
J4		137mm 30mm thick	Gilt	$9.95
J4-A		137mm 30mm thick	Silvered	9.95

MEXICO

THE COMMEMORATIVE
OF MEXICO

The late President John F. Kennedy was very popular in Mexico, and many Mexican people felt an intense sense of grief at his passing. The Central De Numismatica Y Medallistica, V. Carranza 50 Mezzanine, Mexico 1, D.F., issued the above commemorative medal.

The medal was originally supposed to have five different reverses in as many different languages: English, Spanish, French, German, and Hebrew. However, this was changed, and there are now thirteen different reverses.

The medals are proof finish with a matte bust of Kennedy. Struck in 1964, there are a total of seventy-eight different pieces in gold and silver.

The reverse of some of the medals has the words ''Central Numismatica Mexico'' at the bottom, but others do not. As of this writing, the reason for this diversity is not known.

NO.	SIZE	DESCRIPTION	ORIGINAL PRICE
M1	50mm	Gold, fine, English	$66.00
M1-A	50mm	Gold, fine, Spanish	66.00
M1-B	50mm	Gold, fine, French	66.00
M1-C	50mm	Gold, fine, German	66.00
M1-D	50mm	Gold, fine, Hebrew	66.00
M1-E	50mm	Gold, fine, Dutch	66.00
M1-F	50mm	Gold, fine, Irish	66.00
M1-G	50mm	Gold, fine, Italian	66.00
M1-H	50mm	Gold, fine, Russian	66.00
M1-I	50mm	Gold, fine, Portuguese	66.00
M1-J	50mm	Gold, fine, Arabian	66.00
M1-K	50mm	Gold, fine, Greek	66.00
M1-L	50mm	Gold, fine, Japanese	66.00
M-1M	40mm	Gold, fine, English	47.00
M1-N	40mm	Gold, fine, Spanish	47.00
M1-O	40mm	Gold, fine, French	47.00
M1-P	40mm	Gold, fine, German	47.00
M1-Q	40mm	Gold, fine, Hebrew	47.00
M1-R	40mm	Gold, fine, Dutch	47.00

M1-S	40mm	Gold, fine, Irish	47.00
M1-T	40mm	Gold, fine, Italian	47.00
M1-U	40mm	Gold, fine, Russian	47.00
M1-V	40mm	Gold, fine, Portuguese	47.00
M1-W	40mm	Gold, fine, Arabian	47.00
M1-X	40mm	Gold, fine, Greek	47.00
M1-Y	30mm	Gold, fine, English	24.00
M1-Z	30mm	Gold, fine, Spanish	24.00
M1-AA	30mm	Gold, fine, French	24.00
M1-BB	30mm	Gold, fine, German	24.00
M1-CC	30mm	Gold, fine, Hebrew	24.00
M1-DD	30mm	Gold, fine, Dutch	24.00
M1-EE	30mm	Gold, fine, Irish	24.00
M1-FF	30mm	Gold, fine, Italian	24.00
M1-GG	30mm	Gold, fine, Russian	24.00
M1-HH	30mm	Gold, fine, Portuguese	24.00
M1-II	30mm	Gold, fine, Arabian	24.00
M1-JJ	30mm	Gold, fine, Greek	24.00
M1-KK	30mm	Gold, fine, Japanese	24.00
M1-LL	50mm	Silver, fine, .900, English	3.00
M1-MM	50mm	Silver, fine, .900, Spanish	3.00
M1-NN	50mm	Silver, fine, .900, French	3.00
M1-OO	50mm	Silver, fine, .900, German	3.00
M1-PP	50mm	Silver, fine, .900, Hebrew	3.00
M1-QQ	50mm	Silver, fine, .900, Dutch	3.00
M1-RR	50mm	Silver, fine, .900, Irish	3.00
M1-SS	50mm	Silver, fine, .900, Italian	3.00
M1-TT	50mm	Silver, fine, .900, Russian	3.00
M1-UU	50mm	Silver, fine, .900, Portuguese	3.00
M1-VV	50mm	Silver, fine, .900, Arabian	3.00
M1-WW	50mm	Silver, fine, .900, Greek	3.00
M1-XX	50mm	Silver, fine, .900, Japanese	3.00
M1-YY	40mm	Silver, fine, .900, English	2.00
M1-ZZ	40mm	Silver, fine, .900, Spanish	2.00
M1-AAA	40mm	Silver, fine, .900, French	2.00
M1-BBB	40mm	Silver, fine, .900, German	2.00
M1-CCC	40mm	Silver, fine, .900, Hebrew	2.00
M1-DDD	40mm	Silver, fine, .900, Dutch	2.00
M1-EEE	40mm	Silver, fine, .900, Irish	2.00
M1-FFF	40mm	Silver, fine, .900, Italian	2.00
M1-GGG	40mm	Silver, fine, .900, Russian	2.00

M1-HHH	40mm	Silver, fine, .900, Portuguese	2.00
M1-III	40mm	Silver, fine, .900, Arabian	2.00
M1-JJJ	40mm	Silver, fine, .900, Greek	2.00
M1-KKK	40mm	Silver, fine, .900, Japanese	2.00
M1-LLL	30mm	Silver, fine, .900, English	1.00
M1-MMM	30mm	Silver, fine, .900, Spanish	1.00
M1-NNN	30mm	Silver, fine, .900, French	1.00
M1-OOO	30mm	Silver, fine, .900, German	1.00
M1-PPP	30mm	Silver, fine, .900, Hebrew	1.00
M1-QQQ	30mm	Silver, fine, .900, Dutch	1.00
M1-RRR	30mm	Silver, fine, .900, Irish	1.00
M1-SSS	30mm	Silver, fine, .900, Italian	1.00
M1-TTT	30mm	Silver, fine, .900, Russian	1.00
M1-UUU	30mm	Silver, fine, .900, Portuguese	1.00
M1-VVV	30mm	Silver, fine, .900, Arabian	1.00
M1-WWW	30mm	Silver, fine, .900, Greek	1.00
M1-XXX	30mm	Silver, fine, .900, Japanese	1.00

CHAMIZAL MEDAL NO. 1

Mexico has issued two distinct medals to commemorate the signing of the Chamizal Treaty. This treaty returns to Mexico a small strip of land which was formed from a change in the course of the Rio Grande in 1864. The president of Mexico at that time was Benito Juarez. In 1963, President Kennedy and President Adolfo Lopez-Mateos completed final details of the settlement of this issue. The medal was struck in 1964.

The obverse portrays Presidents A. Lopez-Mateos, Benito Juarez, and John F. Kennedy (right to left). To indicate the cooperative feeling between the United States and Mexico, clasped hands are shown—to signify agreement between the two countries upon settlement of a boundary dispute that lasted for one hundred years—together with the word "AMISTAD" (Friendship).

The reverse shows the United States and Mexican flags crossed in front of balance scales of justice.

The strikings are proofs.

NO.	QUANTITY	SIZE	DESCRIPTION	ORIGINAL PRICE
M2		41mm	Gold	$90.00
M2-A		41mm	Silver, .980	6.00

175

CHAMIZAL MEDAL NO. 2

Mexico has issued two distinct medals to commemorate the signing of the Chamizal Treaty (see Chamizal Medal No. 1). The medal was struck in 1964.

The high relief figures of Presidents Juarez, Lopez-Mateos, and Kennedy are finished in frosty matte against a proof field.

The reverse shows the two flags in frosty matte against a proof field, and a draftsman's divider indicates the new boundaries.

NO.	QUANTITY	SIZE	DESCRIPTION	ORIGINAL PRICE
M3		50mm	Gold, .900	$110.00
M3-A		50mm	Silver, .900	10.00

176

ALPRO MEDAL

Sergio Torres Martinez, Apartado No. 7392, Mexico 1, D.F., made the Alpro Medal available in the United States.

John F. Kennedy was very popular in Mexico, and this popularity is revealed by the many items issued there to commemorate Kennedy.

The Alpro Medal is one of the more beautiful works and it appropriately pays tribute to Kennedy.

Gabriel Sotres designed the medal, and it was privately struck in Mexico City.

NO.	QUANTITY	SIZE	DESCRIPTION	ORIGINAL PRICE
M4	600		Gold	$90.00
M4-A	1,000		Silver	6.00

GREAT PRESIDENTS
OF U.S.A. MEDAL

This proof was produced by Centro Numismatico of De-Mexico.

NO.	QUANTITY	SIZE	WEIGHT	DESCRIPTION	ORIGINAL PRICE
M5	20,000	42mm	33 grams	Silver, .925	$12.50

SOUTH AMERICA

SOUTH AMERICAN
KENNEDY HALF DOLLAR

The exact origin of this piece is unknown. It is distributed by Nerio Bustos Rodriguez of Buenos Aires, Argentina. The obverse and reverse are the same, and the medal appears to have been cast from a mold crudely made from an actual United States Kennedy Half Dollar.

It is a very scarce item, and only one is known to exist in the United States. Available information indicates that the few that were made have been destroyed because of lack of interest in South America. This should become a highly sought after item for collectors. It has a plain edge, notched right and left of medal.

NO.	QUANTITY	SIZE	DESCRIPTION	ORIGINAL PRICE
SA1		30mm	Zinc	$3.00

SWITZERLAND

HUGUENIN MEDAL

Honoring John F. Kennedy, this medallic portrait of the late President by the medalist Jean Ramseier has been struck and issued by the Swiss firm of Huguenin Medailleurs.

The medalists were not certain as to the total mintage of these items, but up to the present time they had struck in the amounts shown in the table below.

This medal is unusual in appearance and appears to be a different approach to medallic art than we have seen before. The field is a textured, brushedlike surface.

The medals were also sold by Ateliers d'Art, Huguenin Freres, Medailleurs, Le Locle, Suisse.

NO.	QUANTITY	SIZE	DESCRIPTION	ORIGINAL PRICE
S1	40	60mm	Gold, .750	$175.00
S1-A	150	60mm	Silver, .925	9.30
S1-B	400	60mm	Bronze	3.50

HUGUENIN MEDAL NO. 2

This is the second medal of President Kennedy struck by Huguenin Medailleurs. It is as well executed as the first (see No. S1).

Medal No. 2 is uniface with a profile obverse. Jean Ramseier is the designer. Less than 1,000 were struck in all sizes.

NO.	QUANTITY	SIZE	DESCRIPTION	ORIGINAL PRICE
S2		40mm	Gold, .925	
S2-A		30mm	Silver, .925	$3.00
S2-B		22mm	Silver, .925	2.50

 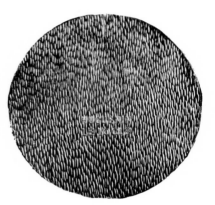

YUGOSLAVIA

YUGOSLAVIA
MEMORIAL MEDAL

This medal was struck in Yugoslavia in 1965.

NO.	QUANTITY	SIZE	DESCRIPTION	ORIGINAL PRICE
Y1			Base metal	

ABOUT THE AUTHOR

Aubrey Mayhew is relatively new to numismatics. He began as a novice collector of United States coins only three years before this book was written. His interest grew, and he soon looked to more rewarding fields. This search took him to medal collecting, beginning with his now award-winning collection of Robert E. Lee coins, medals, tokens, and related items. He went from Lee to Alaska items. By this time, he was set in his direction. Medals were challenging and intriguing; they were educational and demanded time and study. The search and research, unending and revealing, took him to many unexpected and interesting places.

Mayhew lost all sense of commercialism regarding his new-found interest and became a religious student of numismatics, specializing in medallic art. His collecting interest and study increased his desire for a more active and contributing position in the field. When President Kennedy was assassinated, Mayhew began his Kennedy collection, which is considered today the most complete set known. His research stimulated the writing of this book.

Mayhew's entry into the field of numismatics came at a time when the hobby was plagued with hoarders and profiteers.

Had it not been for his own insight and his exposure to some of the more astute collectors, he might have scuffed off the hobby as just another passing interest.

Every collector seems to follow the same essential pattern, and Mayhew was destined to ply the same trails. The hobbiest usually starts with what is commonly called the "shotgun approach"—that is, collecting at least one of every date and variety of coins, tokens, medals, and allied forms of numismatica. Time and economics usually have a way of mellowing the collector to a point of decision about what interests him most from his economic position and about what area he should concentrate on.

Mayhew came to this crossroad very quickly. Born a Southern "gentleman," his main interest centered around the medallic history of Robert E. Lee. What evolved was an award-winning collection nurtured and acquired through intense diligence and travel.

He has only been in the hobby a few years, yet he has made a mark for himself as an astute collector and a knowledgable researcher.

INDEX

PART I—UNITED STATES COINS, MEDALS, TOKENS
AND RELATED ITEMS

Kennedy United States Half Dollar 1964   3
John F. Kennedy Inaugural Medal 1961   5
The Kennedy-Johnson Medal   6
1962 Annual Assay Commission Medal   8
1964 Annual Assay Commission Medal   8
John Fitzgerald Kennedy Memorial Medal   10
Four Assassinated Presidents   11
Presidential Art Medal   12
Kennedy-Pope John Peace Medal   14
The John F. Kennedy Memorial Citizenship Award Medal   16
Manship Medal: The Official Inaugural Medal Commemorating
   the Inauguration of John Fitzgerald Kennedy as 35th Presi-
   dent of the United States of America, January 20, 1961   17
NCS Memorial Coin-Medal   23
Kennedy Memorial Medal by Heraldic Art   25
Kennedy Credo Medal   26
The N.O.T.S. Medal   29
The Kennedy-Johnson Campaign Token   30
Inaugural Ball Medallion   31
The Kennedy-Day Postmaster Medal   31
Erie-Eternal Flame Medal   32
Kennedy Brothers No. 1   33
Kennedy Brothers No. 2   33
Cook County Medal   34
Presidential Art Charm   34
The John Kennedy Memorial Medal   36
Democratic National Convention Token   37
Lincoln-Kennedy Cent 1964   37
1965 United States Spoof Set   38
Presidential and First Lady Medal   40
Vindication of Right Medal   41
JFK Famous Quotation Charm   42
Aetna Vindication of Right Medal   43
Aetna JFK Famous Quotation Charm   43
Tribute to Greatness Medal   44
C.C.O.A. Medal   45
John Fitzgerald Kennedy Commemorative Charm-Medal   45
Cut-out Kennedy Half Dollar   46
LBJ-JFK Token   48
Steinberg-Kennedy Bust   49

Kennedy Ring   50
The Kennedys Medal   50
Lincoln-Kennedy World's Fair Medal No. 1   51
Lincoln-Kennedy World's Fair Medal No. 2   52
Lincoln-Kennedy World's Fair Medal No. 3   52
Wendall-Northwestern Memorial Medal   53
JFK-White House Medal   53
Kennedy Family Charms   54
Sculptured Coin   55
Lucky Penny No. 1—"Memorial Highway"   55
Lucky Penny No. 2—"In Memoriam"   56
Lucky Penny No. 3—"Kennedy-Johnson"   56
Kennedy Plaque   57
John F. Kennedy Elongated Cents   58
Osborne Token Series   60
Manship-Copy Medal   62
Ask Not-Torch Medal   63
President and Vice-President Inauguration Medal   63
35th President Charm   64
Boston Marching Group Inaugural Parade Medal   64
Kennedy-Ask Not Charm   65
Kennedy-Dawn Charm   66
Elongated United States Coin Memorials   66
Profile in Courage Medal   68
Men in Space Medal   68
White House-D.C. Medal   69
Miscellaneous Charms   69
Miscellaneous Key Rings   71
Miscellaneous Kennedy Plaques   73
Miscellaneous "Ask Not" Series   74
Miscellaneous Jewelry Items   79
Kennedy-Whiskeytown Medal   82
NTA Presentation Medal   83
John F. Kennedy Life and Achievement Series   83
Kennedy-Howden Medal   85
Janon "Ask Not" Medal   86
Assassination of John F. Kennedy Medal   86
Hatfield-Kennedy Medal   87

PART II—FOREIGN MEDALS, COINS AND TOKENS,
   BY COUNTRY

ARABIA
Five Rupees of Sharjah   93

AUSTRIA

Champion of Freedom Medal   99
Weltz Memoriam Medal   100
Kennedy Common Good Medal   101

CANADA

Canadian Tribute Medal   105
Kennedy Coin Memorial   106
Rohde Medal   107
Gold Kennedy Medallion   108
Elizron Medal   108

CHINA

Kennedy-Hong Kong Medal   111

ENGLAND

Catholic States Medal   115

FRANCE

Kennedy Cancer Appeal   119
The French Medal Club Medal   120

GERMANY

Political Leaders of the World Medal   123
Kennedy Assassination Medal   124
Kennedy Death Medal   126
Argenteus Death Medal   128
Argenteus Death Medal No. 2   129
JFK Visit to Europe-1963 Medal   130
Argenteus Visit Medal   131
Kennedy-Liberty Medal   132
Shriver-Kennedy Peace Corps Medal   132
Kennedy-Adenauer Medal No. 2   134
Kennedy Welcome in Germany Medal   135
Holl-White House Medal   136
Holl Memoriam Medal   137
Nummis Mundi Medal—"Coins of the World"   138
Kennedy-Adenauer, Munich Medal   139
President Kennedy "Memorial"   140
Kennedy-Peace Dove Medal   141
JFK-Torch and Bell Medal   142
Steinberg-Kennedy Inauguration Medal   143
Feig Memorial Medal   144
Feig Memorial Medal No. 2   145

195

Jacqueline Kennedy Medal   145
Berlin Wall Medal   146
Draped Cross Medal   146
Preissler Medal   147
Men and Ideas Medal   147
Great Catholic Men Medal   148
Three Great Presidents Medal   148
Argor Memorial Medal   149
Kennedy Gold Stamp   149
Philatelic in Gold   149

HOLLAND
Civil Rights Act Medal   152
Dutch Peace Corps Memorial Medal   153

ITALY
Fossa Memoriam Medal   156
Khrushchev-Kennedy Medal   156
Affer Liberty Medal   157
Pirrone-Kennedy Medal   157
Inauguration Speech Medal   158
Memorial Medal of John F. Kennedy   158
Kennedy Presidential Seal Medal   160
Italian Kennedy Assassination Medal   161
Cocepa Medal   161
Inauguration Commemorative Medal   162
Fossa-Kennedy Medal   164
Kennedy-Pope Paul Peace Medal   164
Milan Sport Center Medal   165

JAPAN
"In Memory of" Charm   168
Japan Memorial Medal   168
Kennedy Lighter   169
Kennedy-White House Lighter   170

MEXICO
The Commemorative of Mexico   172
Chamizal Medal No. 1   175
Chamizal Medal No. 2   176
Alpro Medal   177
Great Presidents of U.S.A. Medal   177

SOUTH AMERICA
South American Kennedy Half Dollar   181

196

SWITZERLAND

Huguenin Medal   185
Huguenin Medal No. 2   186

YUGOSLAVIA

Yugoslavia Memorial Medal   189